THIS FAR BY FAITH

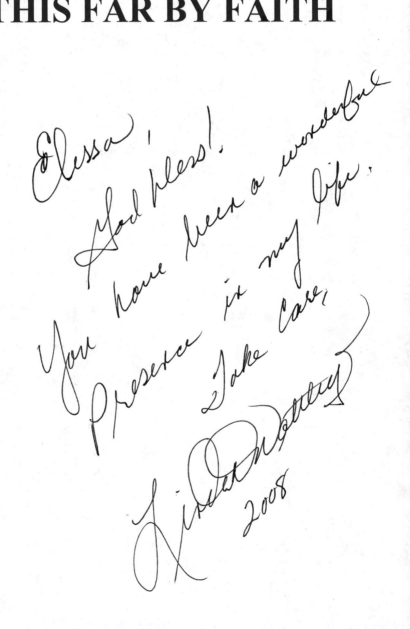

Elissa,
God bless!.
You have been a wonderful
presence in my life.
Take Care,
Lisa McMurtry
2008

Check out these other books by Vanessa Miller

Former Rain

Abundant Rain

Latter Rain

Rain Storm

Through The Storm

THIS FAR BY FAITH

Stories of Hope and Victory Through Jesus Christ

An anthology edited by

Vanessa Miller

Butterfly Press, LLC
Dayton, Ohio

Published by Butterfly Press, LLC

Butterfly Press
5523 Salem Avenue
PMB 257
Dayton, OH 45426

ISBN 0-9728850-5-6

PUBLISHER'S NOTE

This anthology is a work of fiction and true life testimonies. All names, characters, places and incidents in the short stories are either the product of the author's healthy imagination or are used fictitiously and any resemblance to actual persons living or deceased, business establishments, events or locations are entirely coincidental. Each testimony is based on true life situations the author experienced or has personal knowledge of. Each author is individually responsible for any known inaccuracies.

Cover Design by Candace K

This anthology is dedicated to all the This Far By Faith contributing authors who have allowed God to take them on a FAITH journey. Don't ever stop believing...

Table of Contents

Introduction

This anthology was inspired by God. See, I'm no one special, just a girl who grew up on the low income side of town with a dream in my heart. I knew from the time I was nine years old that I would become a writer. However, I had no idea how my dreams would come to pass. But then one day, two years ago as I was on a flight from Dayton, Ohio to Houston, Texas to do a book signing event; it hit me. I was living my dream and it had all come to pass simply because I chose to believe that the God I serve is well able to make me what He wants me to be.

Then the Lord dropped it in my spirit that I had come **This Far By Faith**. I wanted to shout the victory, but since I was still strapped to my seat, I leaned back into my seat, exhaled and said, "Wow."

The thought of coming so far simply by trusting God and stepping out on the faith that was within me was awesome to me. I began to think that there had to be other people in this world with testimonies of faith. God has brought so many of us through the wind, rain and storms of life, simply because we decided to trust Him. That's when I began meeting some awesome men and women of faith. They told me stories that brought tears to my eyes and pulled at the strings of my heart. I knew that my readers would want to know about these testimonies. So I compiled them in this anthology.

I hope you enjoy reading about the faith journey of the contributing writers of this anthology. But more than that, I hope this anthology launches you on your on journey of FAITH!

God Sent Me an Angel
By: Vicki J. Austin

On my sick bed I lay
Many nights turned to day and,
I wonder between states of
Consciousness,
Ponder between snatches of falling in and out of sleep,
Perhaps, I should just give up.

A tender touch lighter than a caress
Whispers "fear not, there's no need for distress".
"Just close your eyes and rest,
I am here, to cradle you through these trying times"

I looked up at the ceiling thinking,
I had dreamed that voice
But with a feather like touch, she
 Told me to "REJOICE"
Soothing finger tips stroked my hair line
And without speaking, I thought in my mind
"You're an angel"

Without speaking back her words filled my head
"God wants you whole, but Satan wants you dead"!
 I know my God in an intimate way'
 Sometimes I feel HE can't hear me when I pray!
I have prayed for deliverance, my purpose for being
I told Him, "I'm spiritually blind, I need Your guidance for
seeing."

Prayed for the ones I love and those I don't even know
Is He turning a deaf ear to me, and if yes, why so?

I have cried out in the darkness when I could see no light
I cried when I needed someone to hold me, stay with me through
the night.
Just felt alone and washed up, tired of this earthly fight.
But there was no one I could see, no one there in sight.

"SSHHUUSSHHH" she said softly and as sweetly as a lullaby
He has seen your many tears and dried your weeping eyes.
God has not wrath for you
You are precious to Him too,
 but as one of His children, you've got to go through
"Through?!, go through? (I sighed) it is all I do
But will the time ever come when I feel satisfied and renewed?

For my strength is weak and I've been tried
When I could fully see you, I thought I had died.
For so long as I've fought the battles that come my way
I am just weary and worn
My spirit has been wounded, now tattered and torn
I believed things would be easy once I was reborn.......

"Ummmm" she said, "you thought life would be easy when you
gave your life to Christ?
Have you given much thought to what he sacrificed?
You are no different from him,
He was persecuted, beaten,
then hung by his limbs.

You think you are suffering and that is true
But God has started a good work in you.
If you hang on a little longer, believe a little harder in your worth
Eventually you will see the fruits of your rebirth
He never said it was easy but to fight the good fight

Using His written word, His Power and His might."

The tempo she continued humming was like medicine to my soul
"You mean I'm not dying?"
No, God wants you whole.
So the Glory of the trials you have withstood
Show you and others who doubt Him He's Mighty, God is good!

Just rest, rest now comfortably
Get you some sleep,
I herald His message; your soul he shall keep
You have been bent, but you didn't break
He loves you dearly, you were not a mistake

I understand I whispered very low
I believe God had not let me go
I didn't know what to think
For usually we are in synch
But His thoughts and ways are higher than mine
Everything is done in the fullness of his time.

I have to work on patience, what a difference it makes,
Just knowing that He has brought me this far by faith.

So be at peace and close your eyes
God never sleeps, the almighty, the wise
I am here child to show you the way
And to confirm to you God hears what you pray.

Vicki J. Austin resides in San Antonio, Texas with her 17 year old son Deondre'. She is also founder of S.W.I.F.T. Inc. A Women's Organization that gives back to the community. Contact Vicki at: email: vickiaustin22@aol.com

Hannah's Faith
By: Vanessa Miller

I'm going to kill him, Hannah thought as she listened to the business like tone of the man on the other end ask, "Is Mr. Thomas Elk in?"

She tightened her grip on the receiver. Every time she answered the phone and heard that professional tone of the person asking to speak with her husband of sixteen months she learned about another past due bill. "He's not in right now. I'm his wife, can I help you?"

"Mrs. Elk, we've been trying to reach your husband concerning some very important personal business."

Hannah rubbed the spot on the left side of the back of her neck where hair used to reside. Her hair had slowly fallen out as each layer of her husband's ten-thousand dollars worth of *personal business* was revealed. "What's this about?" she asked.

"Tell your husband that if we don't receive a payment by next week, we're coming to pick up the car."

She closed her eyes as several strands of hair drifted toward the carpeted floor. She placed the phone back on the receiver and grabbed the keys out of her purse. "So that's why he's been keeping his car in the garage and driving mine. She was getting so tired of the deception. When they were first married she sat down with her husband and mapped out a plan to pay every single creditor he had. She'd even taken money out of her 401-K to make it happen within the eight month period they'd allotted to get it done.

She opened the garage door, got in her husbands silver and black Lincoln and backed it into the driveway. She turned off the ignition, got out of the car and said, "Come and get it."

As she turned to walk back into the house she saw Thomas pull into the driveway with another source of deception. His son.

When they were engaged, Thomas claimed to be just as childless as she. He said he wanted nothing more than to have a child with her, so that he could finally be a father. But seven months after they were married a summons for a paternity test appeared in their mailbox. Thomas swore on a stack of bibles, "That kid ain't mine. His mama is just trying to put him off on me so she can get some child support." She should have known he was lying then. If the woman was after child support she would have picked on someone other than 27,000-a-year-earning Thomas Elk.

But even lying on a stack of bibles couldn't change a child's DNA. Thomas was the father. "Hey baby," he said as his four year-old mini-me tossed a baseball to him. "Why'd you take my car out of the garage?"

Hannah turned and stared at them. How could he not have known that this child was his? They had the same sandy brown complexion, same crooked smile. They even walked the same: head tilted to the side, favoring the right leg, so the sole of the shoe wore down on the right side first. *I swear to you, baby, I'm not J'Laquan's father*. Those words of her husband's rang through her ears every second and fourth Friday through Sunday of the month. She hadn't married a doubting Thomas, hers was a liar, and a deceiver. And she was sick and tired of playing his games.

"While you're out playing with that baseball, the creditors are looking for your car. I'm not going to help you hide it from them." She opened the door and turned her back on her husband and his prodigal seed as she went inside their small house.

They'd bought their home as soon as her husband's credit problems had been cleared up. She was proud of their accomplishments and had once thought of this house as cozy. But when J'Laquan came to visit, she could find no place to hide. The living room and dining room connected and the kitchen was so small you could barely turn around in it.

Standing in the dining room she debated her escape when J'Laquan walked into the house, stood in the living room and said, "Hi, Hannah."

Hannah wouldn't even look at him. He was just trying to let her know that she hadn't said a mumbling word to him, and she was not about to have her manners corrected by a four-year-old. She waved her hand in the air as she stood in the dining room. "I'm a little upset right now, J'Laquan, I don't feel like talking."

Thomas closed the door as he walked in. He snapped at Hannah, "You don't have to treat him like that Hannah. None of this is his fault."

She knew it wasn't J'Laquan's fault. She didn't want to mistreat him, but no matter how she tried, she couldn't force herself to do right by this little boy who had invaded her life. Instead of addressing the issue, she verbally attacked her husband. "You are the most irresponsible man I know. You know we've got all these bills, but are you out trying to get a second job." She pointed at the baseball in his hands as though it offended her and continued, "No, you're out playing catch." She rolled her eyes and walked out of the room.

***

Thomas lowered his head. Defeated. That was how he felt. He had hoped that she would never find out about his most recent financial woes. He'd worked three doubles in the last two weeks to come up with the extra money he needed to pay his car note. He mailed the check into them yesterday, just as he'd told them he would. *Why did they have to call his house and upset his wife?*

He handed the baseball and mitt to J'Laquan and told him, "Take this stuff to your room and change out of those dirty clothes while I talk with Hannah."

"Okay." J'Laquan headed toward his room, then stopped and turned back around. "Hey, Dad?"

"Yes, son?"

"I had fun playing catch with you today, but if it's going to upset Hannah we don't have to play anymore." J'Laquan's shoulders slumped as he turned and walked toward his room.

Thomas watched his son walk away. It tore him up to see the little guy so sad. He wanted to tell him that Hannah wasn't upset with him. But the boy was smart; he knew mistreatment when he was receiving it. Thomas knew what it felt like also. His shoulders slumped just like his son's as he turned toward his own bedroom.

He put a smile on his face as he opened the door to his bedroom. The smile faded as he watched his wife throwing her clothes into an overnight bag. "What are you doing?"

"You're a smart man, figure it out." She opened the dresser drawer and pulled out some of her under clothes and tossed them in her bag as well. "I cannot stay here one second longer. I need some time away."

His wife was the most beautiful woman he'd ever come in contact with. And although he loved her olive skin tone, hazel eyes and high cheek bones, it wasn't her outer layer that most attracted him. She had a big heart. She was giving and understanding. She had walked through the fire with him, and helped him to become a better man. But lately, it seemed as though her inner beauty was fading. Still, he didn't want to live a day without her. "Don't leave, Hannah. If this is about my car note, I paid it yesterday." She kept packing. "Stop this honey, I can explain why it was late."

She ignored him as she tried to open the bottom dresser drawer. The handle broke off in her hand, and she swung around to face her husband with the object held high. "Do you see this? You promised we would get a new bedroom set, but did I get it?"

15

Hannah's mother had given them their bedroom set and the cream colored leather sofa and chair in their living room as well. But the bedroom set was more than a decade old when she'd passed it down to them. The wood had faded in spots and bubbled in others. He'd wanted desperately to buy his queen something she could be proud of – he'd wanted to be someone she could be proud of. He hadn't brought much of anything to this marriage. Well that wasn't true – he'd brought ten thousand in debt and a four-year-old son. Neither of which Hannah appreciated. "I'm working on it. If you give me some time, I'll make good on all my promises to you."

She harrumphed as she put the last of her items in her overnight bag and zipped it. "Time is running out on your caviar dreams and Champaign wishes."

Bringing his voice to a whisper he told her, "I didn't expect to be paying child support. I'm trying to get adjusted to having three-hundred dollars a month taken out of my paycheck. You helped me with all the debt I had when we first got married, why can't you work with me on this?"

Rolling her eyes for the second time that day, she picked up her bag, opened the bedroom door and walked past him. "I'll be at my sister's for the weekend. Will talk when I get back."

***

Hannah sat in her sister's expansive kitchen dipping her fresh out of the oven oatmeal cookie into ice cold milk. Her favorite remedy to the blues. Her big sister knew her so well. "Janice you just don't know what it's like. I can't take it anymore. Thomas was not truthful with me and I shouldn't have to stay married to a man like that."

Janice put another batch of oatmeal cookies in the oven and sat down behind her island and put her elbow on the marble counter top. "What makes you think I don't know how it is?"

16

Hannah put another warm, ooy-gooy cookie in her mouth and waved her arm in dramatic fashion. "Look at all you have. This huge house with non-hand-me-down furniture is evidence enough that your husband treats you good. This place has to have at least 4,000 square-footage."

Janice laughed. "4,500 to be exact. But little sis, I think you are forgetting something."

"You're doggone right, I forgot something." She stepped down from the high backed stool and walked from the kitchen to the Great Room. The name was no exaggeration, from the cathedral ceilings to the Pella windows and the open fire place, not to mention the snow white carpet and lounging furniture - spectacular. "I forgot how to live good, is what I forgot." She turned to face her sister as she heard foot steps behind her. "I feel like I live in a shoe when I come over here. Everything is so big and roomy, while I can barely turn around without knocking something over in my house."

Janice put her sister's hand in hers. "It didn't start off like this, Hannah." She squeezed her sister's hands. "Don't you remember that little apartment John and I had on Wabash?" Janice laughed as she released her sister's hand. "Girl, some days I thought the roaches were eating more food than we were."

"I remember that apartment."

"Come sit with me," Janice told Hannah. They walked out of the snow-white room and entered the family room. The place for all things beige and comfortable. They sat together on the sectional and Janice told her. "It took a lot of years before John and I were able to live comfortable. We struggled for the first nine years of our marriage."

Hannah knew all about struggling. She was majoring in it – at the school of hard knocks. "Didn't you get tired?"

"Of course I did. Those were the nights when I did a lot of crying and a lot of praying. I still can't explain how it all worked

17

out; I just know that God answers prayers. And I think he has a special place in his heart for a crying woman."

A tear trickled down Hannah's cheek. "But John didn't have to pay child support or spend time with a child that didn't belong to the both of you."

Janice wiped the tear from her sister's face. "No he didn't, but he had other problems, and so did I. But we worked together to solve them. I'm telling you what I know, Hannah. With God's help you can get through this."

Head bowed low, Hannah confessed, "I haven't prayed much lately."

Janice scooted closer to her sister and put her arm around her. "God's still on the throne, sweetie. He hasn't changed residence – you can still find Him if you seek after Him."

She and her sister talked well into the night. Then Janice told her that she needed to go make her man happy. Hannah went to the guest room and climbed in bed, but she couldn't get to sleep that night. She was too busy wondering why she couldn't get past the anger and work with Thomas. If her sister could work with her husband, and move her family from poverty to prosperity why couldn't she do the same? Why was she so angry all the time? Her husband was good to her, and she loved him.

At about three in the morning she finally admitted to herself where the greatest part of her anger stemmed from. She hadn't conceived. She and Thomas had been trying to have a baby for over a year – and nothing. She didn't have many childbearing years left. If something didn't happen soon…

And every time she saw J'Laquan, it was like a reminder of her failure to conceive a child for the man she loved. Consequently, even surrounded by her husband's love, she was miserable.

She told Thomas how she felt a couple months back, and he'd asked her, "Isn't my love enough for you, Hannah?" She pulled the covers tightly around her barren body. She hadn't been able to

18

answer his question then, and she still didn't know if his love was enough to quite the turmoil in her soul.

***

On Sunday morning Thomas got up early to make J'Laquan's favorite breakfast: cinnamon pancakes with chocolate milk. Thomas was learning more and more about his son each weekend they spent together. He enjoyed getting to know J'Laquan. The only unfortunate part of the time he spent with his child, was his wife's reaction. But he had denied and neglected J'Laquan for too long as it was, there was no way he would continue to be a dead beat dad. Yeah, he was paying his child support. But sending money didn't make you a dad. Families, invested time in one another. Thomas decided that if he only got one thing right in this life – he wanted to be a great dad. He wanted his son to grow up and tell his sons that he had a father who did everything he could and even went that extra mile to ensure that he lead a successful life.

The telephone rang as Thomas sprinkled powdered sugar on J'Laquan's pancakes. He hoped it was his wife, calling to say she was on her way home. But a glance at the caller ID told him it was his best friend, Sam Johnson. Thomas smiled. This was probably his first smile since Hannah walked out on Friday. Sam was his boy. He had the ability to make him believe that everything would be alright. They'd been boys for along time. They went to the same elementary, same high school. Played on the same basketball team, went on double dates together. Married months apart from each other. They'd done everything together. Well, everything but…

"You still coming to church with me today?" Sam asked after Thomas picked up the phone and said hello.

Sam had given his life to Jesus without Thomas' consent or approval. These days Thomas' opinion didn't seem to carry much weight with Sam. It was all about how the Lord expects him to live, and what he discovered in prayer. And now his boy was getting baptized. "Man, I totally forgot."

Sadness crept into Sam's voice. "Don't tell me that you won't be there. This is a really big event in my life."

Thomas wasn't a total heathen. He'd grown up in church after all. He knew how important baptism was. "I didn't say I wasn't coming. I just said I forgot. We'll get dressed and meet you there in an hour."

***

Hannah went to The Church on the Rock with Janice and her family. The praise and worship was electrifying. She couldn't remember when she had last lifted her hands in praise, but as the praise leader ushered the congregation into the presence of the Lord, Hannah lifted her hands and worshipped God. After praise and worship seven congregants were baptized. Thomas' friend Sam was among them. Seeing Sam, made her long for her husband. She lost a bit of her praise as sadness crept in.

But when Pastor Frankson stood behind the podium, it was as if he made it his own personal business to preach her happy. She started wondering why she and Thomas didn't attend church more often. When they were first married they discussed how they wanted to raise their family in church. Maybe the fact that she hadn't been able to provide Thomas with a child had halted all thoughts of attending church. As if seeing into the depths of her wounded heart, Pastor Frankson started talking about how his children were the joy of his life. Tears rolled down Hannah's face as she sat in her seat. She wanted so desperately to have a child. Someone to call her own. But maybe she had waited too long for marriage. She was thirty-seven and her eggs had dried up.

When Pastor Frankson finished preaching, he made an altar call. Hannah remembered her sister saying that God had a special place in His heart for crying women. She stood, and walked

20

toward the altar. But she didn't allow the altar workers to pray for her – she needed a direct line to God. Hannah bowed down at the altar, with tears streaming down her face she admitted to God that she was mad at her husband and mad at his son because she had been denied the opportunity of being a mother.

Her lips were moving but no sound escaped as she continued to sob and pray – pray and sob. "Lord," her silent lips proclaimed, "I feel so empty without a child of my own. My husband loves me, I know that. But I need to be able to give him a child. Please help me."

She then began to tell the Lord how sorry she was for neglecting to spend time with Him. "I've missed You, Lord. I won't forget about You again. I promise."

***

Thomas and J'Laquan arrived at The Church on the Rock twenty minutes late. The place was so packed he doubted they would find a seat. But a kindly greeter hugged them and then directed them to a seat in the back.

He missed praise and worship, but arrived just in time to give his offering to the Lord. He was so glad he hadn't missed offering. From a child his mother and father taught him about bringing his first fruits into the house of the Lord. He'd always been diligent about doing just that. But the last two years had thrown him for a loop. He'd gotten off track with attending church – he hadn't been a regular since he left his parents home, but he had attending at least once a month so he could pay his tithes. He'd also gotten off track with paying his tithes. He quickly calculated his week's earnings and put ten percent of that into the collection plate.

When the pastor stood up to preach, Thomas spotted Hannah in the second row. Try as he might, he couldn't keep his mind focused on the message, his eyes kept slipping in the direction of his wife. When the altar call was made and Hannah stood up looking lost, bewildered and tormented, Thomas couldn't help but wonder if he was the cause of her pain. "Lord," he proclaimed with his head bowed, "I won't ever neglect to pay my tithes again, if You could just bring a bit of happiness into Hannah's life again."

He lifted his head just as his wife fell down at the altar. He wanted to go to her, but from the distance she looked like a mad woman, a drunk even, as she cried and rocked, her mouth moved so fast, he doubted if any sound escaped at all. How could he go to her, if he was the reason she was at the altar displaying herself in such a manner? Maybe it was time for him to let her go. He leaned over and told J'Laquan, "Gather your things, we need to go."

The boy was on the floor playing with his X-Men figures. He looked up. "But nobody else is leaving," J'Laquan told him.

Thomas picked the X-Men off the floor and stood. "Let's go."

***

Driving home, Hannah felt renewed. She couldn't explain why she felt different, except that she knew this time, God had heard her prayer. She'd had an audience with the King. She'd received quite a few funny glances as she removed herself from the altar. She even heard a little boy ask his mother if she was drunk. But she didn't care. Her time with God had been just what she needed. God had renewed her faith. She was now headed home to work on her marriage.

She thought about calling Thomas to tell him she was on her way, but she had treated him so bad and had such evil thoughts of him the day she left, she was afraid of his response. She thought their reunion would go better if they were face to face, and he saw how sorry she was. Then maybe he would forgive her. As she pulled into their driveway she saw Thomas and J'Laquan in the back yard tossing that baseball again. Irritation crept in. She tried to shake it off as she closed her eyes and prayed, "Lord, please don't forget me. If you give me a child, I promise I will give him back to You. I will raise him to love and serve You."

What about the other child, Hannah? Who will give him back to Me?"

Hannah's mouth fell slack as she pressed her hand against her chest. "My Lord? Are you speaking to me?"

I want J'Laquan to serve me also, Hannah.

Tears began to roll down her face. Was she really that selfish? Had she only thought of her own feelings and neglected all thoughts of what J'Lquan needed. What she'd discovered today was that not only did she and Thomas need God in their life, but J'Laquan needed God also. At his young age, the only way J'Laquan would come to know God would be through the adults he came in contact with. "Lord, forgive me. Help me to show that little boy Your love."

As she got out of the car the bitterness surrounding the three hundred a month Thomas sent to J'Laquan's mother slipped from her heart. With each step she took toward her husband and his child she saw more of what J'Laquan needed from her and less of what she thought he was taking. As she rounded the corner, she wiped at the tears on her face and tried to smile.

J'Laquan had the baseball in his hand. He was getting ready to toss it to Thomas when he spotted her. He lowered the ball, then hid it behind his back. Hannah walked over to him, bent down in front of her adorable stepson. She held out her hand and asked, "Can I throw the ball to you, honey?"

J'Laquan's eyes widened. "You want to play with me."

Hannah wiped more tears from her face. "Yes, I want to play with you. Is that alright?"

J'Laquan wrapped his small arms around her neck and squeezed. "Don't cry Hannah, I'll toss the ball to you."

Thomas joined his wife and son and wrapped his arms around both of them. As he said, "Thank You, Lord, for giving me back my family."

Hannah lifted her head and looked at them. That was it, wasn't it? You might be able to pick your friends, but family was a whole nother matter. Sometimes families were good together, sometimes they weren't. But her job was to pray about the things that concerned her and have faith enough to believe that God could turn things around.

Vanessa Miller is an author, playwright and motivational speaker. She writes life changing Christian fiction and currently has five novels: The Rain Series (Former Rain, Abundant Rain and Latter Rain) The Storm Series (Rain Storm and Through the Storm). She has also written four stage-plays. Vanessa lives in Dayton, Ohio with her family and attends Revival Center Ministries, International.

Contact Vanessa at: www.vanessamiller.com email: vmiller-01@earthlink.net

HOPE REAWAKENED!
By: Vanessa A. Johnson

After fourteen years of being unable to conceive after the birth of my first son, my husband and I thought that we weren't able to have more children. Although I hadn't taken precautions for seven years, I didn't get pregnant. Imagine our shock when we found out I was pregnant again.

I've always had an irregular cycle. When I began experiencing stomach problems I attributed them to stress. The thought of being pregnant was the farthest thing from my mind.

I assumed I'd developed an ulcer. After weeks of tests, with negative results my husband suggested I take a home-pregnancy test. My initial reaction was, "He must've bumped his head or something!" But I took the test anyway; mainly to shut him up.

Could it be possible? I wondered. *Yeah right*, I told myself as the little plus sign turned pink. When I thought about all the tests I'd taken in weeks past to determine why I wasn't feeling well and all the time I was pregnant, I just shook my head. *How could the doctors have missed that diagnosis?* I wondered.

I scheduled an appointment with my Primary Care Physician, who confirmed the pregnancy. I couldn't wait to tell my husband, which meant I'd have to admit he was right!

Afterwards, I scheduled an appointment with my OB/GYN, who confirmed I was fourteen weeks pregnant. But the ultrasound immediately revealed an abnormality.

We were told if we continued with the pregnancy, the baby would probably die before I delivered. The baby's urethral valve was blocked.

We were sent to a specialist in high-risk pregnancies. My husband and I discussed the situation and concluded there was no way God would allow me to become pregnant and not let this

25

child be born. Hope had been reawakened after fourteen years and I wasn't about to give up.

Despite the dire warnings from the specialist to terminate the pregnancy, we couldn't and remained firm in our decision to continue with the pregnancy.

The following week I returned to my OB/GYN. I informed him of my visit with the specialist. I told him that I was never going back to see that specialist again. This was the day before Thanksgiving, 1993. My OB/GYN told me to go home, he'd be in touch.

On my way home, my husband paged me to get in touch with my OB/GYN, a.s.a.p. When I did, he excitedly informed me there was another specialist at another world-renowned facility that he wanted me to see.

He explained, "This specialist is well-known for doing exceptional things for high-risk pregnancies. I've already scheduled your appointment for next week."

It was evident I wasn't willing to give up hope and my ob/gyn wasn't giving up either.

Thanksgiving was indeed filled with prayers of thanks.

The specialist told me about an experimental surgical procedure. "The procedure involves inserting a long needle through your stomach to the baby's abdomen, extracting the excess fluid and inserting it back into the amniotic sac. But because of the amount of fluid that's already accumulated, there's no time to waste. I need to perform the surgery today if your baby has any chance of surviving."

I agreed and immediately called my husband. He rushed over. The procedure was successful. I was released the following day and scheduled to return in one month.

At that appointment the specialist discovered that the fluid had accumulated and he needed to perform the drainage procedure again. He said, "Due to the blockage, the fluid will continue to accumulate and this concerns me because it's hindering the baby's kidney and lung development. There's a new medical device, a shunt, which was invented in England that we could use. The shunt has to be ordered and will take a few weeks to arrive."

The shunt was ordered. He performed the drainage procedures weekly as we waited. The downside to having the procedure so frequently was that it caused me to go into premature labor.

I was sent home with a prescription for Brethine to stop the contractions. Because I couldn't keep any food or liquid down, I was dehydrated, which also caused premature labor.

The shunt arrived and was inserted successfully. I resumed my normal activities.

A month later, we learned the shunt had performed properly, but the fluid had begun accumulating because the baby had now outgrown the shunt. It was evident my little miracle was fighting to survive.

The drainage procedure was performed on a weekly basis again. Upon being discharged the following morning, I was placed on a home monitoring system whereas my contractions were electronically transmitted to registered nurses, who then reported the results to the specialist. The shunt was indeed operating properly.

A representative from my insurance company stated that if I didn't remain on bed rest, the company would stop paying for my medical expenses. The specialist was in agreement with this stance too. He stated he didn't realize I was still working.

Weeks later, the specialist said he couldn't risk prolonging the delivery any longer because the baby's kidneys and lungs were in jeopardy of not properly functioning with the constant fluid buildup. He decided to deliver my baby on February 17, 1994.

But on Friday, February 11th, 1994, I was involved in an automobile accident. My vehicle was struck and pushed into a telephone pole. I wasn't wearing my seatbelt. Upon impact, I jumped atop the vehicle's console and held onto the steering wheel to keep from being thrown through the windshield.

I was transported by ambulance to the hospital where the specialist was on staff and remained there throughout the weekend as I again began to experience premature labor.

I was released on Monday, February 14th, and scheduled to return on Wednesday, February 16, 1994 to have the drainage procedure done before the delivery.

I received a general anesthesia for the delivery by cesarean section on Thursday, February 17, 1994. My baby weighed three pounds, twelve ounces. He was bigger than the specialist predicted, but some of his weight was attributed to the fluid inside his abdomen.

Just as miraculously as his journey to birth, Jalen responded positively to every poke, needle prick, and test administered during his two month stay in the Neonatal Intensive Care Unit. Everyday I talked, sung, hummed, massaged, held and rocked Jalen.

Jalen was released from the hospital on April 16, 1994 and continued progressing.

On July 28, 1994, my birthday, Jalen suffered his first setback. He successfully underwent Mal-rotation intestinal surgery. He was discharged on Monday, August 1, 1994, and continued progressing until that dreadful day, Monday, September 19, 1994. Three weeks after my mother's sudden death, Jalen contracted pneumonia.

In the Pediatric Intensive Care Unit, he appeared to be improving but was prematurely removed off the ventilator on Thursday, September 29, 1994. The following morning on September 30, 1994, I experienced a hell like never before. Jalen suffered cardiac arrest and died and at that moment all of the hope I had, seemed to die with him.

Looking back on my pregnancy and Jalen's birth it was miraculous that he survived despite the huge mountains he had to climb. It is often said that everything happens for a reason. I take great comfort in knowing that the procedures performed during my pregnancy became a part of medical books. It helps to know that what we went through might help another family who has to travel the path we've been down. This means that Jalen's life and the struggles we endured surely weren't in vain.

Five years later, my husband and I learned that hope hadn't died after all, that it had only been asleep. On January 18, 1999, hope was awakened when our daughter, Alexis, was born; healthy. There were no complications experienced during the pregnancy.

While one child cannot replace another child, when I look into her eyes I feel like I'm looking through her to him. When I look at her, I am reminded that hope never dies. Sometimes hope takes a rest somewhere between faith and love and can very well be awakened with just a little nudge from God.

Vanessa Alexander Johnson, a life-long Louisianan began writing in 1994 after the untimely deaths of her mother and son. Her first book, When Death Comes a Knockin' is a self-help, inspirational book about loss and grief. (Lulu Press, 2005, ISBN 1-4116-2470-X)
Contact Vanessa at: www.vanessaajohnson.com email: vjohns1@bellsouth.net.

Your Will Be Done!
By: Gerri Leggett

Jessica stood in front of the door of her one bedroom apartment staring at the deadbolt, scared to open it. She prayed she had waited long enough for David to get to work before leaving. If he had doubled back she would surely be in trouble. David had put in the deadbolt lock nine months ago when he came home and found her outside talking to a neighbor. "What are you doing outside?" he yelled.

"The air conditioner is broken. I got hot and came out for some air." Jessica spoke softly with a lowered head.

"Get inside," he demanded, "There ain't nothing wrong with that air conditioner, I unplugged it. You don't need to be in here running up the bills."

"But this is Arizona, its 90 degrees outside and it feels like 100 inside." She couldn't believe he was serious about her not leaving the apartment. Where would she go? He drove the only car they had and they lived in the middle of the desert in a small town away from everything but military life.

"Don't you leave this apartment unless I tell you to," he snapped

"Okay," she whispered.

Over the past year of her marriage, David had become very controlling. She remembered when they dated, he would always check on her whenever they weren't together. He would call her to see where she was and whom she was with. Her mother told her that David wasn't letting her breathe. But Jessica thought that David's actions showed his love and concern for her.

He told her long hair made her look too trashy, so she cut it in a bob. Her mother told her he had her cut her hair because he didn't want any other guys looking at her. "Jessie, God made you a beautiful black woman and don't you let anyone tell you different," her mother said.

David had a way of making Jessica second guess everything about herself. He was never affectionate anymore; they hadn't touched each other in over six months.

David began locking Jessica inside the apartment after he found her sitting by the pool in a swimsuit he'd picked out for her. "Did I say you could come outside half naked?" He threw a towel at her and made her get up and go inside.

A young man by the pool said, "Baby you look too good to have some busta talking to you like that."

Jessica looked back and David grabbed her by the arm and dragged her inside. "You're hurting me, David."

"You hurt me when you disrespect me like you did today; letting everybody look at your body and talk to you like I'm not your husband?"

He sounded so sad, Jessica felt bad for hurting him, so she began to apologize. "Just don't let it happen again," he snapped, then asked, "What's to eat?" He never put his hands on her; but he did frighten her.

She ran into the kitchen and began cooking for him even though she didn't have much of an appetite.

***

The next day Jessica received a certified letter, but she couldn't open the door to sign for the letter. She opened the window and told the postman she had lost her key to the deadbolt. He passed the letter through the window and went to the apartment office and reported it to the manager. The letter was from her mom. She opened it and found an abundance of scriptures like: In God I trust, I will not be afraid. What can man do to me? (Psalm 56:11); God did not give us a spirit of timidity, but a spirit of power of love and of self-discipline (2 Timothy 1:7); There is no fear in love. But perfect love drives out fear (1 John 4:18). At the end of the letter her mom wrote, 'baby, please pray that God's will be done in your life!' Suddenly, Jessica began to cry uncontrollably. How did her mother know what she had been going through?

The doorbell rang again; it was the manager, Mr. Roberts. She wiped her face and opened the window. He told her he had a spare key and handed it to her. She thanked him an instantly hid it.

After receiving the letter from her mother, Jessica prayed for weeks for God's will to be done in her life. She never used the key the manager gave her, for fear that David would find out. She read her mom's letter over and over and began to read the small bible her mom packed in her suitcase a year ago.

Not knowing how or where to begin, Jessica would open the bible and read whatever scripture was on the page, (Psalm 40:8) states, I desire to do your will, O my God; your law is within my heart. She closed the book and opened it again. (Psalm 143:10) read, Teach me to do your will, for you are my God; may your good spirit lead me on level ground. Instantly Jessica remembered the day she married David, everything went wrong. Her dress was torn, so she had to wear a sundress, the Chaplin on base would not perform the ceremony without counseling first, and the chapels were all full. Jessica was so upset she ran into the restroom and called her mom on her cell. "Baby, if you were in the will of God this would not be happening. God is blocking this union for a reason, please don't do this."

David began banging on the door, "Girl lets go! I found someone to do it." Jessica told her mom she would be okay and hung up. They were then married in a small room covered in red velvet with dim lighting. They didn't need a marriage license or a witness. They stood in front of an old man who said, "Do you take her and do you take him?" They both said, "Yeah." and the old man said, "Okay, pay the clerk." David gave the clerk fifty dollars and she handed him a paper that said they were Mr. and Mrs. David Prescott.

***

Jessica never saw their marriage document after that day. Now looking back, she didn't even remember seeing her full name on the document. Was she even married? She cried, "God, I need you now, help me Father teach me your will. Father, guide me with your counsel; do not turn a deaf ear to me. Let your will be done!"

Jessica began her search for the marriage license and found it pinned inside the pocket of his uniform from boot camp. Like she thought, it didn't have her name on it. She called the manager's office and asked if he had a copier. She opened the door with the spare key he gave her that she kept pinned to her bra like she saw her big momma do when she was small. She ran to the office and handed the paper to the manager. He read it and asked. "Why do you want to copy this?" "I need a copy of my license to send for my birth certificate."

"Jessica, I used to work at the county courthouse. This is not a legal marriage license. I can fax a copy to a friend at the courthouse and find out for sure if you would like?"

"Yes, Mr. Roberts, I would really appreciate that." He called his friend, informed him of the fax and sent it over. Jessica jumped every time she heard a car go by. Within minutes Mr. Roberts's friend called him back. Mr. Roberts informed Jessica that the license was illegal; and that the police closed the place where they had their marriage performed. He also said all marriages performed there would be annulled." Jessica stood there with her mouth agape.

"Oh!" Mr. Roberts snapped his finger. "I have a four hundred dollar check for you."

Jessica looked at the check with her name on it, and wondered where it came from?

"You gave it to my wife when you first moved in to attend the cosmetology school she manages. Since you never started, she asked me to give it back."

"Thank you so much Mr. Roberts and thank your wife." Jessica forgot about the school, David had told her that he didn't want her washing people's hair and gossiping all day. She took the check and her copy of the license and put them inside her bra and ran all the way back to her apartment. Once inside the apartment, she folded the original license nice and tight the exact way she found it and put it back. She made sure everything was in the right place and then began cooking. While the food cooked she called the airlines and got some price quotes for a one-way ticket from Arizona to Georgia. Her only problem was that she had to leave from Phoenix, which was two hours from where she lived. Jessica remembered a prayer she often heard her mother recite; For I know the plans I have for you declared the Lord (Jeremiah 29:11). She prayed harder than she ever had for God to help her to become the woman he planned for her to be.

Jessica stepped out on faith. "Lord if this is your will, everything will work out fine." The ticket was on sale for one hundred ninety-eight dollars. She had three days to cash her check and get to the airport. Most importantly, she had to find someone to give her a two-hour ride to Phoenix.

David kept her inside so much that she didn't really know anyone. Each day she packed a little more of her things and put her suitcase back where it was. It was Thursday morning and David was ready to leave at 5 o'clock as usual. Jessica lay in bed with her eyes closed pretending to be asleep. When she heard his car leave, she immediately jumped up and ran to the window to make sure he was gone. She then got on her knees and began to pray. She still didn't have a ride to the airport and a cab would probably cost as much as her plane ticket.

She heard David pushing his shoes and boots around in the closet before he left, so she began pulling them out. In one boot she found sixty dollars and in another boot she found pictures of a female. She put back everything and started to walk away but changed her mind. She turned around, bent down, grabbed the boots out of the closet, snatched out the money, looked at the photos and anger took over. "This is probably why you haven't touched me in six months." She said as she ripped the photos and placed the torn pieces back inside the boots and threw them back in the closet.

She took a shower, dried off and put on her robe. She put her suitcase on the bed, what should she wear? She didn't realize she had lost weight since she moved to Arizona. None of her favorite tops fit her right anymore. Stuffing her clothes back into her suitcase, she remembered an outfit her mother had sent her for her birthday. David told her it was too tight, so she never wore it.

She reached under the bed and found it still in the box it had been shipped in. Inside was a pair of designer jeans with pink stitching, and a pink top. Jessica always thought her mothers taste was a bit too conservative, but the outfit *was* the right size.

She stood in the mirror, the outfit looked perfect. She stared at herself for a while wondering when she had become a fool for this man. A man who didn't physically abuse her, but he certainly did verbally and mentally abuse her on a regular basis. She was no longer afraid to be the Jessica her mother raised, and was ready to begin living her life again; out of bondage. She stood in front of the door scared to open it, when she heard a voice whisper, *God did not give you a spirit of fear.* She then took a deep breath, unlocked the door and started knocking on her neighbors' doors in search for anyone who could give her a ride. When she turned the corner, she saw a young man going into his apartment. "Excuse me, I know you may just be getting home and you don't know me, but I really need a big favor."

"What can I do for you, Sistah?"

"Will you please drive me to the airport in Phoenix?"

"That's a two hour drive, what time do you need to be there?"

Jessica looked at her watch it was 7:15a.m. "I have an 11:30a.m. flight, but I need to be there by 10:30a.m. to pick up my ticket."

"I guess we need to get going then," he said.

Jessica grabbed him and gave him a hug "Bless you. I'll go get my bags." She ran back to her place and grabbed all her bags off the bed. By the time she dragged them to the door the young man was ringing the bell. He put her bags in the trunk and they were off to the airport after Jessica had him stopped at the bank so she could cash her check.

They reached the airport at 9:45a.m. He stopped and got Jessica something to eat. She went into the airport paid for her ticket and checked her bags. She took the sixty dollars she had gotten out of David's boot and gave it to the young man for his help. He gave her a hug and whispered in her ear, "You deserve so much more than him. I'll pray you find God's perfect will for your life." He held her hand and told her to keep her head up and ran off. As she watched him disappear in the crowd, she looked down, opened her hand and saw he had given her the money back. She began to cry as she realized she didn't even know his name. "He was my angel sent from Christ!"

***

When she arrived in Georgia her mother was there to pick her up. "Baby whatever you went through, God has delivered you from it."

"Momma, I know I didn't want to hear you back then, but as time went on I heard you loud and clear." They hugged, got her bags and were on their way home.

"Do you want to get a bite to eat baby?"

"Sure." They went to a nice soul food restaurant for lunch. "Momma, David and I were never really married."

"What are you talking about?"

"I mean, I found out the place where we went to get married was a fraud and I can get our marriage annulled."

"To God be the glory, you can sever all ties to that man and move on with a fresh start," her mother said. They ate their food and listened to a live jazz band play. Jessica hadn't felt so good and free in over a year.

They asked the waitress for the check, but she informed them that the gentleman at the front had already taken care of it. He was walking over to them when Jessica began to smile. "Hello Mrs. Lovejoy how are you?"

"Wesley Brooks how are you doing, young man?"

"I'm doing fine, ma'am." He turned to Jessica and said, "Hello, Jessica, how have you been?"

"Fine," she responded. Then added, "Thanks for paying for our lunch."

"You are welcome; I hope to see you again. But I have to get back to work right now," Wes said.

Mrs. Lovejoy said, "Here's Jessica's number, give her a call."

"Momma!"

"Thank you Ma'am, I'll call you, Jessie." Wes said.

"Okay, bye Wes," Jessica said, then turned towards her mother. "Momma, why did you give him my number?"

"Girl you are not dead, he may be God's will for you."

"I don't know if I'm ready to start dating." Jessica whispered.

"Did you know Wesley is the new youth minister at our church?"

"Wes Brooks is a minister? When we were teens he wanted to be a doctor."

"He's a good minister. You have a ministry too; you are still an anointed dancer. Maybe it's time you start dancing for the Lord again."

"Maybe I do need to get back into church, I just still don't know if I should be dating."

***

A few months had past, Jessica hadn't heard from David or Wes. It was Friday evening; Jessica was lying on the sofa watching television.

The phone rang and Jessica jumped. "Girl it's been three months and you're still jumping when the phone rings. You're no longer married to that man; there is nothing he can do to you." Mrs. Lovejoy said and picked up the phone. "Hello Lovejoy residence, how can I help you?" she asked.

"May I speak to Jessie?" A suave male voice sang threw the telephone.

"Who's calling please?" Mrs. Lovejoy asked curiously.

"Wesley Brooks"

"Hold on please.' She covered the receiver and quickly stated, 'Jessie its Wesley girl, get the phone." Jessica jumped up off the sofa dusted her pants, fixed her hair, and checked her lipstick. With her hand still over the phone, her mom said. "Jessie, baby, he's on the phone and he can't see you."

"Oh yeah, I'm just a little nervous." Jessica took the phone from her mother, cleared her throat and softly said, "Hello." She spoke to Wes for hours and made plans to go out to dinner after service on Sunday. A month after she returned home, Jessica had begun dancing at church again. She really did enjoy getting back into her ministry. She had already done a solo that had the congregation and ministers in tears.

***

Sunday service was great. The presence of God was definitely in the sanctuary. Pastor Dukes had everyone on their feet praising God. After service Jessica and three other dancers were in the restroom changing.

"Jessica, you want to go with us to get some dinner," Amanda asked.

"Thanks girl, I wish I could, but I have plans."

"Hello Mrs. Lovejoy." The ladies said simultaneously. "Hello ladies, you all had the anointing of God on you today."

"Praise God, thank you." Amanda responded with her hands raised.

"Jessica, I came to get your bag and take it home for you." Her mother said

" See you later, Jessie." The ladies all waved as they left the restroom.

"See you all at rehearsal." Jessica replied. Once everyone was gone, her mom helped her get ready. She prayed with her and headed home.

Jessica walked out of the restroom in a beautiful little black dress that was both classy and a bit sexy. Standing by the wall across from the restroom was Minister Wesley Brooks speaking with Deacon Alexander. Jessica smiled at them.

Deacon Alexander came over to her and grabbed her hand. "Sister Jessica you are truly an anointed dancer, it is good to have you back with us."

"Thank you, Deacon." She looked over again and Wes was gone. She said her goodbyes and went outside. Wesley stood by a black Jag looking handsome as always. Jessica took a deep breath and walked over to him. "You look lovely, Jessie." Wes said

"Thank you, Minister Brooks. You look handsome yourself."

"What's with this Minister Brooks stuff? We've known each other most of our lives. Please call me, Wes."

"Wes, I cannot believe you're a minister now."

He held the door for her, walked around the car and got in. "When you allow God to truly order your steps, He will work in mysterious ways."

"Wes, you truly said a mouth full."

They had a wonderful date remembering when they were sixteen and mad about each other. They remembered telling each other their plans for the future. He was to be a doctor and she was to open a dance studio. "I guess God had other plans for us." She said.

"God's will for our lives have been deterred by us. We kept getting in His way. Now that we've allowed Him to run things, He's made me a doctor, over souls. You still have the ministry of dance. You touched all of us with your solo last Sunday. I can still see you opening your dance studio. I've been in prayer for a wife, yet I've got in God's way choosing all the wrong women, and God said no. I waited for Him and He showed me a woman sitting at a table in a pink top in my dreams. The next day I saw you from behind eating with your mom. I got a knot in my stomach. You wore a pink top and blue jeans. I didn't know it was you until I paid for your check and you looked over at me. That's when the knot in my stomach really got tight. I still had feelings for you, so I had to pray a few more months to make sure. God kept showing me you in my dreams. Jessie, you are the one for me."

Jessica was shocked, she too had been praying and God showed her Wes in her dreams. They dated for six months before they got engaged, Jessica opened a successful dance studio, and they were married a year later by Pastor Dukes after completing marriage counseling. God's will was finally done!

Gerri Leggett a native New Yorker, is a phenomenal flourishing author, residing in McDonough, GA with her loving husband Kenneth and two beautiful children Amanda and Alexander. God has gifted her to write. Over the years she has written many plays, spoken word and skits for her church. This is her season to allow the world to experience the anointed gift God has placed in her! The best is yet to come. Other Works: *In The Midst Of It All!*

Contact Gerri at: email: gleg@bellsouth.net

Three Times the Blessings
By Angelia Moore

"Sure, you can have whatever you like, since you have had the miscarriage." the nurse said nonchalantly.

"What, miscarriage?" I asked, then as realization struck me I screamed, "No, no, no!" I cried, became angry and cried some more. Why? How could this have happened? I did everything I thought I should have; why did I lose my baby?

That was the 12th week and 4th day of my first pregnancy; and month after month, year after year – I waited to hear that I was pregnant again. The doctors said nothing was wrong.

We continued to help our family with their children, siblings with my nieces and nephews... nieces and nephews with my great nieces and nephews. My husband and I decided, maybe that was our calling; to be there for those who needed us most. It had been 2 ½ years since my miscarriage. We had looked into adoption and decided to just wait – be patient and the Lord would provide. However, I must admit – getting my cycle monthly was the most heart wrenching experience. It was a total of 31 cycles and nothing.

April 1, 1999 – Surprised with a new beginning

Then one day as I sat at the hospital waiting on my 18 month old great niece to come out of open heart surgery, I saw a beautiful little girl sitting in a pumpkin seat between my sister and cousin. My heart melted. "She is beautiful, whose baby?" I asked my cousin.

"Her name is Lisa and she can be yours if you want her. This is "Nika's baby. The state is going to terminate her rights and I am not trying to be anybodies Momma," Sarah, my cousin, responded. "She and her brother, Lemont are going up for adoption soon. They have been living with me for a while in foster care."

42

Sarah gave me her phone number and the number to the case manager. I put it in my purse thinking, nothing would come of it. That evening I shared the events of the day with my husband. He said, "Yeah right, who just finds a baby at the hospital?" Two months later we were in classes to become foster and possibly adoptive parents.

You could not image how many people are involved in the foster care process; the case manger, the Guardian ad Litem, the Adoption Specialist... The list goes on and on. Since I was now working in the child welfare system, I knew some of what we would go through. But nothing could prepare me completely.

As time past, we went to court, completed our classes, got criminal history checks, visited with the kids, and had the kids come and stay with us. We enjoyed it, we were scared senseless, but we walked by faith.

The children finally came to live with us permanently in January. We had taken a few weeks off work to be with the children. We allowed them to visit Sarah and other family members at least 8 times in the first three months. By May 2000, everything was going well; my husband, the children and I had come to love each other and were becoming more bonded each day. I must admit, we were very excited about the opportunity to be parents. We prepared to meet with the case manger and the child welfare staff to receive their approval for the adoption. As I am getting ready to leave my office to go to the meeting; my phone rung. It was my Aunt Mattie. She tells me that Sarah changed her mind and wants the children back. My heart broke. I cried, screamed, prayed, yelled, and then I stopped. I called my husband, the case manager and the Guardian ad Litem. I had no idea what to do. I was confused, devastated and not sure if this could really happen. Could we actually have the children in our home; love them, bond with them and then have them snatched away by one phone call. Everyone I called said the same thing; be still – we will find out what is really going on.

The child welfare professionals stated that they would support our adoption petition for the adoption of Lemont and Lisa. However, the adoption would be contested; the judge would ultimately decide.

I would like to explain something right here. I have never fought for anything; I always allowed the desires of others to decide the ultimate decision. My husband, church members and I prayed for guidance. Thank God for the proper mate, he asked simple questions to me…. "Are you doing this for you or for the children? What will happen if she changes her mind again? We made a commitment to them, we told them we would be here for them, are we going to let them down as well?" Well, that made things super clear. My children, our children, our beautiful, wonderful, precious gifts from God were more valuable to me than making things easy for the adults involved. So, as their mother and father, we went to court and fought for our children.

The last hearing was in March, we were told the judge might decide that day. I decided to fast from March 1st until 16th (the day of the hearing). The judge did not decide that day, but I decided to continue my fast (of red meat and sweets) until he ruled. By mid April, I began to feel a little sick and light headed. I thought the stress of the trail and turmoil of the hearings and the fasting were taking a toll on me. I contacted my doctor and asked if he would prescribe something for the nausea. He asked if I could be pregnant, I snickered, pregnant? Uh, no, it had now been 3 years since, my miscarriage, there is no way I could be pregnant especially not now, that we were in the midst of this adoption and trying to find out if we're keeping out two children. However, the doctor insisted that we do a pregnancy test. It was positive.

Our adoption was final June 14, 2001, what a wonderful Father's Day gift. I gave birth on November 23, 2001. My

44

husband says, "God allowed us to go without birth children, in order for us to be open and available for the blessing that Lisa and Lemont were. Then he blessed us one more time, with Leon. What an amazing, wonderful, fearful, stressful, powerful, and humbling experience.

Angelia L Moore, and her husband reside in Indianapolis, IN. They are the proud parents of 3 wonderful children (their fourth due in May '08). Knowing that God is faithful has gotten me through many trial and tribulations. I count my family (immediate and extend) as part of the rock that sustains me. Thanks to God for all He has done.

Contact Angelia at: email: anjeemoore@yahoo.com

Don't Worry About A Thing
By: Vette Berrian

My name is Vette Berrian and I have learned that God is on my side, no matter what I go through, if I just trust in the Lord I can get through anything.

My parents weren't real church goers. We attended services on Easter Sunday mostly. Other than that it was weddings and funerals.

My brother and I visited grandma during the summer. Grandma was the church-goer of the family. She was in church every time the doors opened which was most of the time. Grandma went to a holiness church. You know the ones where people jump up all of a sudden and run around the room. Or they shout, fallout and speak in tongues. This was a strict church with definite rules about how a young lady should carry herself. In other words: no make-up, no wearing of pants and you waited until marriage to have sex.

Something about church made me happy. I loved going; hated leaving. I felt the Lord's pull early. As a child I asked Him into my heart. So I attribute most of what I learned about the Lord to my grandma. When I was at grandmas I was on the straight path. However, when I went home I fell off course.

There are many things in the Bible that we see figuratively. For instance, "Take up your cross and follow me." I saw this as literary symbolism. The Lord didn't really expect me to strap a 150 pound tree to my back and walk around in pursuit of Him? Did He?

But there are other passages that must be taken literally. This would include Proverbs 18:21 which says, "Death and life are in the power of the tongue." In other words, watch what you say or what you wish for. Because you just might get it.

46

Over the years I have asked the Lord for many things. Mainly men. For some strange reason I couldn't live without them. I wanted love and I thought it came from them. There was a void in my life that I tried to plug up with men. Maybe it stemmed from not growing up with my biological father. I had a great father figure at home. My stepfather was a good man, that didn't matter. All I could see was that the man that helped conceive me wasn't a part of my life.

I didn't wait for the Lord to send me my special someone. God was busy and needed my help finding Mr. Right. Therefore, I gave myself to more broken men than I care to count. Men who were neglectful, deceitful, unfaithful and who in turn betrayed my love. My life was completely out of control. And with each failed relationship, I would ask the Lord to forget.

It took several years for me to realize that I had been trying to mend a broken heart with men instead of seeking after God's unconditional love. That realization was the first step in my recovery. I decided I didn't need a man, I *wanted* a man. Believe me there is a big difference between the two.

One day I decided to let go and let God. I was tired of being with men who didn't deserve me. I said, 'If God has a man for me, he is going to have to find me, because I won't be looking for him. I am tired of not getting what I deserve."

Sure it took me many relationships and two failed marriages to get there. Don't laugh. The point is - I got there. Or at least I thought I had. Seven months after I stopped looking for a man I was blessed with Frederick Scot Berrian.

Scot and I met in Colorado Springs in the summer of 1994. I knew not long after meeting him that he was the man I had been made for. He was a true gift from God and proof that GOD does answer prayer. Scot was handsome, selfless, sensitive, loving, hardworking, educated and funny. He was just what the doctor ordered.

We dated for two years. It wasn't an easy two years. I was given a true gift. But I misused and mistreated that gift. I didn't believe I was worthy of great things even though my heart knew it. I thought I had let go of the past but the truth was, I hadn't. In my mind I was unforgivable. I was still hanging on to every mistake I had ever made. I let those mistakes define me. Therefore, I was unforgiving, bitter and angry.

I blamed Scot for the mistakes of other men and I subconsciously did everything I could to sabotage the relationship. The heart I was trying to give him was still in a million pieces. Pieces full of hate and mistrust that I picked up daily. In constantly picking those pieces up I made Scot's life unbearable at times. I would not let go of the past. Scot continued to love me anyway.

I wanted to love this man. I did love him. At least the best I knew how. Truth be told - I didn't know how to love. I knew I was ruining one of the best things I had going in my life. I didn't know how to stop it. I wanted to, but didn't know how. So I went to the one person I knew wouldn't let me down - God.

I prayed so many nights that the Lord would change me. Prayed that I would become worthy of God's and Scot's love. I wanted to get on with the life I knew I was capable of living.

Despite how I treated him, Scot asked me to marry him and we were wed on July 13, 1996. A week before we got married we rededicated our lives to God. After rededicating my life to God I started to treat Scot with the love and respect due him. He received all the love and admiration I knew I was capable of giving.

We were both being molded by the Lord and life couldn't have been better. We were happy. Our marriage was good and our children were happy and healthy. Our careers were sky rocketing. Money was flowing. We were being blessed coming and going.

Scot and I grew strong in the Lord. We had weathered many storms and passed several tests. No one could tell us we weren't moving on to bigger and better things.

"I remember several pastors asking, "If you lost everything, would you still follow God?"

Scot and I knew in our hearts "yes" was the right answer. But our minds hadn't thought about the ramifications of the word "everything." Everything means-all. Surely, God didn't mean it literally? Right? God wouldn't allow everything to be taken from us, would He?

Scot and I did lose what we deemed as everything. This ordeal became a true test of our faith.

***

On November 13, 2002, I came home from work with the worst migraine I had ever had. My head was pounding, the room was spinning and my stomach felt like I was on a ride I couldn't get off of. All I wanted was medication, a dark room with a bed and Scot by my side.

As we sat in bed, Scot, my husband of seven years listened as I regurgitated my day through a stream of tears. I was hysterical and inconsolable. Suddenly I stopped talking. Thinking I was tired and just needed rest, my husband helped me to lay down.

The next morning I awoke to a warm voice saying, "Vette time to get up." As I opened my eyes and looked around the room I found I was alone. Then my bedroom door was opened by this beautiful man who stood in front of me in a blue robe. "Good, you're awake," he said. As he continued to ramble I just stared at him in silence. "Vette, say something you're freaking me out."

"I can't," I said.

"Why not?" he replied.

"Because, I don't know who you are, or why you're in my room."

"Vette, stop playing, this isn't funny," the man in the blue robe said.

The look on my face told him I wasn't playing. "I'm Scot, your husband." Silence and a blank stare followed. In the background I

49

could hear children talking. It sounded like they were headed for the room. "We have three children," he said panicked. "Do you know their names?" Nothing followed. With that he turned and said, "Get dressed, I'll be right back."

I'm not sure how much time passed. However, when he returned to the room I was still in the bed. I hadn't moved a muscle. I didn't want to. He came over to the bed and flashed an ID card with both our pictures then a marriage license. Then he said, "I called your mom she's on her way."

A little while later a honey brown woman with short curly hair appeared through the door. "What's up baby?" She said.

"Are you my mom? I asked.

"Yes," she replied.

She asked several questions and then called for Scot. They got me dressed and then took me to Baptist Hospital. My mom, an LPN answered most of the medical questions as Scot chimed in with answers for the general questions. Once the nurse was satisfied that she had enough information she assigned me a room.

"Only one of you can go back with her," she said. At that point I lost it. I started screaming and held onto my mom and husband. I couldn't explain it. I didn't know either of them, but my instincts told me that I needed to stay with them.

Once the doctor appeared and had his questions answered he sent me for all kinds of tests; EEG, EKG, MRI etc… After the tests the doctor stated that a stroke may have caused memory loss even though there was no signs of one in the test results.

In a split second, my life as I knew it had come to an end. I had complete amnesia. I remembered how to talk and walk. I had problems remembering words and constructing sentences. I had no historical life memories.

I had been married seven years to Scot, an Air Force Officer. We had three children: Domenique 11, Q'Ristien 8 and DeVan 7. I didn't remember marrying him or having them.

50

All I remembered clearly when I awoke was "Don't worry about a thing. He's gonna handle everything." It played over and over in my mind against white clouds and a bright light.

During those next few days, mom told me that the words I kept hearing in my head were from a favorite song of mine. It was by Tonex and entitled "Bout A Thing." She said I kept hearing it because God was letting me know that He was still with me. He was using that song to reconnect with me. I didn't remember Him, but He never forgot me.

Shortly after I woke up we found that my personality had changed. I was completely different from my old self. I even started referring to myself in the third person. The woman who went to sleep was not me. *She* was the old Vette and I was the new.

I tried to live life as it had been before. I was married with children. It wasn't their fault I didn't remember them. So I tried to be the old Vette. I tried to live *her* life which included being intimate with Scot. We had sex the first couple of days. I felt I had to do it out of obligation. I was his wife. Isn't that what wives do? But I wasn't comfortable with that. I felt I should know him better. I should feel something for him. Having sex out of obligation, when I really didn't want to; only made me bitter. So I stopped cold turkey. I told Scot, "I don't know you like that!" and he accepted my decision even though it didn't make him happy.

Although I tried to be the old Vette, I wasn't. I wasn't Scot's wife and I wasn't a mother either. I was tired of pretending that it was okay. I told Scot that I wasn't her and if this thing was going to work; he was going to have to get to know me. I wanted my own life and I was no longer going to live a lie.

We spent days trying to get to know each other. The more I found out, the more I was confused. Everything was a joke to him. How could she marry a man like him? Yet everyone who knew me said that I/*she* loved him tremendously and that we were happy. We were "the couple." People wanted to have a love like ours.

I found it all amusing. Because the more I got to know about Scot the less I liked him. But I decided to be committed to keeping the old Vette's family together. I wasn't going to leave. I'd do what was necessary to get along, especially for the children's sake. But I didn't want him romantically.

Scot and I tried to keep the amnesia from the children by letting him answer all their questions. Domenique, the oldest sensed that something was wrong.

We sat the children down and explained what had happened to me. They cried. We cried. "Are you going to die from this?" they asked. We said, "No." How are children supposed to comprehend that the woman that birth them doesn't even know them?

As the days progressed I got more and more angry with God. How could He allow this to happen to me? To my family? Why couldn't anyone find anything wrong with me? If He loved me so much-why? What could I have possibly done to deserve this? I wanted answers.

While I was waging war on God, Scot stayed strong. We had lost my income because I could no longer work. Disability had denied my claim twice so his income was it. We were way over our heads financially and bill collectors were calling daily. Still Scot wasn't moved. He was on the verge of losing his job and he wasn't worried. He was steadfast that God would make a way for us.

Scot had stated on many occasions that I/*she* was very close to God and maybe I should pray. I tried. Nothing. I didn't even know where to begin. However, I was determined to get my answer from Him so I kept trying. I talked to Him like he was right in front of me.

With each passing day, praying got easier and understanding His purpose for my life was becoming clearer. I had rebuilt my relationship with Him. My faith was stronger and I knew I would be okay.

Something else in me changed also. I started to see Scot in a new light. He was a great father and he was always loving, supportive and kind to me-even when I wasn't that way with him. I began to see him the way I imagined *she* saw him. I realized why the old Vette had fallen in love with him. Before I knew it, I was in love with him and I couldn't imagine one day without him in my life.

We renewed our vows on November 12, 2003.

I saw doctor after doctor in the pursuit of a diagnosis from November 2002-April 2004. We wanted to know what happened. Especially, since we were told it could happen again. No one could give a definitive answer. We heard stroke, seizures, aneurysm, multiple personality and a migraine that produced amnesia. Because there was no tangible proof of any of these diagnoses I was sent to mental health professionals.

In the beginning, seeing mental health doctors made me even angrier. They didn't have any answers. In fact, very few of them believed me. I was putting on a show to get attention. Who does that? And how do they keep it up for years without someone close to them noticing?

In January 2004 Scot and I appeared on the Montel Williams Show. Scot being a very private person only agreed to go if it was going to help me get better. Unfortunately the trip didn't get us anywhere medically.

But something happened to me and Scot while in New York taping that show. We connected on a different level. Our love was stronger. Being on that show helped me release the fear and shame I had been feeling over my condition. It was finally out (to millions of viewers) and I didn't have to hide it anymore. I was free to get on with my life: a life that included Scot and three beautiful children.

We gave up on medicine after that trip and looked toward the only person who had never let us down-God. It was at that point that God spoke to me and Scot and healing started taking place.

Something inside of me said you need these people and they need you. Fight your way back to them. That is what I did. I dug deep and turned to the only One I ever really knew-God. The word says "Cast your cares upon Him for He cares for you." I held on to that.

In realizing God cared so much, I was able to completely open my heart to my family. The Father opened my eyes to my families needs. I had not considered that Scot, the children, family and friends had lost their loved one when I surfaced. The old Vette died November 2002. I had to give them time to mourn the woman they loved. Scot lost a wife and the children lost their mother.

Letting them mourn her was hard. There were times when I felt that she was the enemy and I had to compete with her memory. I wanted them to forget about her and just be happy with me.

The Lord showed me that my actions were selfish. I was asserting my place when no one was questioning it. Mourning her didn't diminish their feelings for me.

It's been almost five years since that life altering event and my family is intact. Yes, it was an uphill battle that was full of pain. Getting reacquainted was not easy for any of us. But we got through it together. Leaving wasn't an option on either side. We knew if we held on we would make it.

I still don't remember much about the past. Perhaps that's for the best. Sometimes the past can be a prison cell. Although it helps mold us as people; it also traps us and makes it hard to move forward. I didn't want to remain confined. So I chose to leave the past behind.

We live in the now. We make each and everyday count. Each memory is precious to us. The Word says that tomorrow is not promised and we live like each day is our last.

No, I am not the genius that *she* was. I can't see or hear a phone number now and regurgitate it ten years later without thinking about it. I don't have the gift *she* had for million dollar words. I struggle to find words to make sentences. But God is still good. I am writing again. I thought I had lost that capability. I couldn't have written this story last year.

I am very talented. I can do things that amaze me. I try new things and become amazed at the fact that I can do it. Then I wonder how I knew how to do it. Only to find that it was something *she* knew how to do already. My mind is slowly opening up.

How many of you know that God is a restorer?

One major side effect of amnesia for me is retaining information. I have to write down 98% of what I hear or I'll forget it almost immediately. Therefore, I live a regimented life. I never leave home without my day planner.

Although I still have after effects years later, that's okay. I am grateful for all I do have. I am alive and in good health. Things could have been completely different. I could have woken up not being able to speak at all or having brain damage.

The hardest thing for me is realizing that *she* and I are the same people at different places in life. *She* was a product of her own making. *Her* relationship with God is not my relationship. Our faith is different. I can't say *her* faith wasn't as strong as mine. I don't remember, so I can't comment.

What I do know is; I am what He wanted. I am told that *she* often talked about the person *she* knew *she* could be if *she* could let go. *She* even told Scot there was a better person inside of *her* fighting to get out. I heard that *she* prayed for change. I am the embodiment of what *she* desired to be.

Even though we share the same body; we do not share the same life. I fight daily against glimpses of *her* personality. *She* was angry, defensive and unhappy. I am not. I will never be *her*. I love who I am too much.

I think the Lord saw a broken vessel reaching out. He wanted *her* to be whole and *she* wasn't. There is no way *she* could have served Him in the way He wanted as she was. Creating me changed all of that. I am whole.

Now when a pastor asks "Would you still follow God if you lost everything?" We look at each other and smile. We can truly say "yes". For, we know beyond a shadow of doubt that we are together by the grace of God.

The Call and the Cold War, My Duty and My Destiny
By: Elder Joseph B. Howard, Sr. Th.D.

As the stealth submarine made its way off the coast of sunny and green Ireland, I don't think any artist could have painted the scenic beauty I beheld. God, the great architect, had once again created from nothingness the colors and substance of His tapestry, a page from the Garden of Eden. Suddenly, the tranquility and bliss of the Irish setting was interrupted. A foreshadowing of things to come had just appeared in our view, a foreboding sign of danger. The lookout watch spotted several fishing trawlers about a thousand yards away. The trawlers' eerie crew waved as we approached, appearing hospitable even though there was an obvious ominous feeling to it all. The OOD (officer of the deck) noticed the apprehension on my face, and sarcastically replied, "Don't worry; it's just the Soviets keeping tab on our position and wishing us a safe patrol." I thought to myself, *welcome to the all-too-surreal game of the Cold War. A game most of the world doesn't even know exists.*

My life's journey had begun in the red haze of the steel mills of Gary, Indiana, and would strategically and systematically take me on an odyssey of restoration and spiritual fulfillment. It would send me across the Atlantic Ocean, Europe, the Arctic Circle, to other secret locations, and finally to the brink of World War III. My spiritual destiny was shaped in a million-dollar 460-foot war platform, powered by a nuclear reactor, on our way to stand alone against the great Soviet naval juggernaut. God's sovereignty and grace would find and sustain me underneath the polar ice caps and through the depths of three oceans, where ultimately I would be sanctified by the power of the Holy Ghost to do God's will.

It was March in the year of our Lord 1983. I was stationed onboard the Nuclear Fleet Ballistic Missile Submarine, USS

Lafayette SSBN 616 Blue Crew. We were on patrol somewhere in the North Atlantic. We had lost our radio communication with the fleet, and because of that, we were under orders to assume the great Communist Threat had destroyed communications *and* the United States. So, at this time in history, the captain of a submarine could launch a nuclear pre-emptive strike without permission from the Pentagon or the President. "Mann Battle Stations Missile. Spin up all Missiles. This is the Captain. This is not a drill!" There was a powerful feeling of duty and shock as we went through our paces that had been drilled in our heads countless numbers of times. Stress started to overcome several members of the crew. We understood that civilization would soon be wiped off the face of the planet.

There was a lot of yelling, swearing, and a few minor fistfights as we were brought to the edge of World War III. The devastation of Armageddon would come quickly and decisively. Most of the crew was on edge and it showed. Our lives and the world as we knew it was about to come to an abrupt end. Intrinsically the war had already begun because you realize that a few minutes after you release your missiles, they (the former Soviet Union) will release theirs, and suddenly half the world is a radioactive parking lot!

It takes a special sailor who knows he is staring world annihilation in the face to carry out his assigned submarine duties. We were there for one reason only, and that was if we received orders, we were to terminate with extreme prejudice any country that was preparing to launch nuclear missiles against the United States. This strike would only result in a retaliatory strike against us, and by and large, civilization would be lost. This thought was in the back of every fleet ballistic submariner's mind, but you did your job anyway.

I was performing all the duties I was trained for, but even though my natural man received the natural call of the battle

58

stations alarm, my spirit man was receiving quite a different and just-as-important call from the Father. "Jesus, keep me near the cross," I whispered as I had heard my grandparents say countless times. I was caught in an Ezekiel like out of body experience as I was receiving orders from the captain of the submarine *and* the captain of my soul (Jesus Christ). My transmission from the Father was very present and powerful. My life's purpose had been revealed in the midst of impending worldwide doom.

Through utter confusion and chaos, the Lord brought holy serenity and joy. In the midst of this apocalyptic nightmare, the presence of the Lord was with me. The missiles were spun up and the launch sequence initiated. I should have been numb from fear, but by now, I was in the spirit on the Lord's Day. He assured me this was His day, and I was to rejoice and be glad in it. "For whether we live, we live unto the Lord; and whether we die, we die unto the Lord: whether we live therefore, or die we are the Lord's" (Romans 14:8, King James Version). I did not fear death, because in my heart at this time I knew it was not an option.

The time was near, but instead of the realization of world destruction, I was having my own "Damascus Road" experience. My soul was magnifying God, because I had been called as a laborer in the vineyard. My mission statement was clearly on point. "And he said unto them, Go ye into all the world, and preach the gospel to every creature. He that believeth and is baptized shall be saved; but he that believeth not shall be damned." Mark 16:15-16 (King James Version)

My first boot camp took eight weeks. This spiritual epiphany that permeated my spirit didn't take that long. The embryo of anointing had changed into a fetus of Holy Ghost Power that was nurtured through the umbilical cord of Jesus Christ. My calling to preach the gospel was charged and induced by God. Out of the midst of chaos and impending death and destruction, a new son was birthed. "For if ye live after the flesh, ye shall die: but if ye through the Spirit do mortify the deeds of the body, ye shall live. For as many are led by the Spirit of God, they are the sons of God." (Romans 8:13-14, King James Version).

I was now given in this evolution of equipment issue the whole armor of God that is necessary to be more than a conqueror. I was given the responsibility to share a message of life to a dying world. "How then shall they call on him in whom they have not believed? And how shall they believe in him of whom they have not heard? And how shall they hear with a preacher? And shall they preach except they be sent? As it is written, how beautiful are the feet of them that preach the gospel of peace, and bring glad tidings of good things!" (Romans 10:14-15, King James Version)

I was heralded to spread the gospel to a dying world. I was further instructed (Matt. 28:19-20) "Go ye therefore and teach all nations, baptizing them in the name of the Father, and of the Son, and of the Holy Ghost. Teaching them to observe all whatsoever I have commanded you: and, lo, I am with you always, even unto the end of the world." I knew beyond a shadow of a doubt this was my personal memorandum from God to fulfill my destiny. He promised me that very moment victory and peace in Him if I would submit. "Yes, Lord, whatever you ask, I will do it," I replied.

"Howard, who the heck are you talking to?" My chief was standing nearby, observing my actions.

"Chief, it's okay; you just wouldn't understand."

"I don't need you breaking out into some *old Negro spirituals* right now. I need you focused!"

60

"Aye, aye Chief, I'm focused!" My acceptance to preach was birthed at that very moment. Some of the sailors stationed near me figured I'd cracked under pressure, as some already had. "Thank you, Jesus!" I cried. God tenderly embraced me with His love and gave me gentle assurance that I would be delivered from the snarls of the Soviet Communist Navy. As the confusion and tension mounted, I realized how the other crewmembers must have felt; thinking that half the world in a matter of minutes would be annihilated. Sweat trickled down my forehead as I ran up the ladder to the control center to hand the captain the missile keys. I continued to thank the Lord for the blessed oil of victory and peace He was pouring into my spirit-man.

My mandate was embedded on the imprints of my heart. "Finally, my brethren, be strong in the Lord, and in the power of his might. Put on the whole armor of God, that ye may be stand against the wiles of the devil. For we wrestle not against flesh and blood but against principalities, against powers, against the rulers of darkness of this world, against spiritual wickedness in high places. Wherefore take unto you the whole armor of God, that ye may be able to withstand in the evil day, and having done all, to stand. Stand therefore, having your lions girt about with truth, and having on the breastplate of righteousness; And your feet shod with the preparation of the gospel of peace; Above all, taking the shield of faith, wherewith ye shall be able to quench all the fiery darts of the wicked. And take the helmet of salvation, and the sword of the Spirit, which is the word of God" (Ephesians 6:10-17 King James Version).

Even though I was part of the crew of the *Lafayette,* I was part of a crew far more powerful. I was part of the crew that was addressed to the church at Ephesus. The Apostle Paul's letters once again imparted wisdom unto my heart. "And take the helmet of salvation, and the sword of the Spirit, which is the Word of God: Praying always with all prayer and supplication in the Spirit, and watching thereunto with all perseverance and supplication for all saints; And for me, that utterance may be given unto me, that I may open my mouth boldly, to make known the mystery of the gospel" (Ephesians 6:17-19, King James Version).

Within a few minutes, the announcement was made, "Secure from battle stations missile." The release of tension was so great and overwhelming; many sailors that day should have given their lives to Christ right then and there. There was a great evangelistic opportunity that should have resulted in many souls coming to Christ. Staring at death has a way of letting you know how fleeting and temporary life really is. Even today, I don't need a cheerleader in worship service to pump me up, because I know there's an answer in prayer. "And he spake a parable unto them to this end, that men ought always to pray, and not faint" (Luke 18:1-3, King James Version).

I was born-again to worship the Lord through service. This was my Azusa Street/Upper Room experience. What was actually a few minutes later, but trust me, it seemed like hours, the word was passed that communications had been restored and we were not at war. The order was passed "secure from battle stations!" The crew celebrated and so did I.

While in the midst of my praise, the navigation officer came over to me and whispered, "Petty Officer Howard, I heard and saw what you were doing during Battle Stations!"

I replied, "Yes, sir!"

"Well keep doing it; somebody has to." He whispered, obviously afraid of what the other officers and crew would say if he stood up boldly for Jesus. I answered, "Yes, sir, I plan on it!" I really felt sorry that this man felt the need to whisper and hide his relationship with Christ. I just prayed for him that one day he would stand up and be accounted as a man of faith and conviction. I had no idea this monumental victorious epiphany would become just one of many battles I would face in the upcoming years in another war, the war for my soul.

Elder Joseph B. Howard, Sr. Th.D. is a third generation steel worker. Born amidst the red haze and dust of the steel mills of Gary, Indiana, he enjoyed writing as a child. He is a disabled vet and former pastor of the Sovereign Grace Church in Racine, Wisconsin. Elder Howard is a retired English instructor for San Diego City College and former Dean of the Church of God in Christ Ministers Bible Institute (Milwaukee, Wisconsin). His formal education includes a bachelors of science in Adult Education, a Masters of Art in Biblical Studies, and an earned doctorate in Christian Education.

Contact Elder Joseph at: www.jotreinspirationalbooks.com email: sovgracpstr76@aol.com

The Valley of the Shadow of Death
By: Linda Delany

It was November 28, 2002, providentially my birthday, when the cover and photographs of my first book, *Stewardship: A Matter of Principle – Don't Outsmart 'em, Out God 'em™*, was unveiled to me in a boardroom office in downtown Memphis, Tennessee. A PowerPoint presentation had been prepared and it was accompanied by Mary Mary's musical composition titled *Can't Turn Back Now*. This experience was so emotionally encouraging and spiritually strengthening that I began to release the tension that had been building up for months inside me. I cried a river of tears as if something within me required that I hear and respond to the integrity and the perfect efficacy and essence of God's Word. In spite of worries, I felt God's presence letting me know His promises are true. I knew that I had not been forsaken and God still has many blessings awaiting my arrival. The book was just the beginning of seeing my dreams come true. It was such an awesome and inspiring feeling.

After such an awe-inspiring moment, I was soon brought back face-to-face with my fears. But after such occurrences, faith is increased in the form of God-given strengths.

One of the many things that had occupied my mind over the previous few months was the fact that my sister Dorothy was very ill. Like a roaring lion calculating a pernicious assault on vulnerable prey, cancer had come to confiscate the life of my sister. My family had already experienced the sting of cancer-related deaths in 1998 and 1999 with two of my sisters. I hurt and I privately shed many tears as I talked to God. I shared the desires of my heart with God. Dorothy reminded me, "nothing is lost when you know where to find it." With this, we prayed in agreement that God's will would be done in her life and my own.

I took a deep breath and accepted the fate of the situation. I held to God's unchanging hand to see me through and I knew Dorothy was doing the same.

On February 5, 2003, the sunset of Dorothy's life came. I miss Dorothy, but she is not lost. I know that salvation is as close as your own mouth and heart. Heaven is a prepared place for prepared people. I rest in knowing that I will see all three of my beautiful sisters again.

When Dorothy died my father was in the same hospital around the corner from her in ICU. Dorothy was always a Daddy's girl (much like me) and I knew she dearly loved my father. At 80 years of age, Daddy had respiratory challenges among other medical concerns and we knew that he was knocking on heaven's door waiting to be allowed in. Daddy understood that he was close to death and he had become like a restless soldier in a foreign land with transfer papers in hand. However, God had not chosen to take him yet. It was not easy, but my mother felt that it was important that my father knew about Dorothy's death before she was buried. As she and I stood at his bedside and held his hands, she told him and I silently prayed. He nodded but did not, and perhaps was unable to overtly react. I spent most of the evening with him before leaving to proofread Dorothy's obituary.

On Tuesday, February 11, 2003, the morning of Dorothy's funeral, I didn't get to sleep until around 4:00 a.m. I woke up around 8:30 a.m. looking to see who was shaking me, but no one was there. I was a stone's throw from the church down the street where Dorothy's funeral would be held a few hours latter. I felt a very strong presence, but nothing was audible to me. I immediately called the hospital to check on my father. The nurse with whom I spoke said that all was quiet and normal, but I heard something different in the sound of her voice. I got dressed and called one of my sisters. I expressed to her that I would not be attending

Dorothy's funeral. I had done all that I could do for Dorothy, so I was going to the hospital to be with Daddy.

When I walked into Daddy's room at 9:30 that morning, I could see that he was still experiencing difficulty breathing, but he was somewhat responsive. I held his hand and lightly laid my head on his chest as I prayed and talked out loud to Daddy. Soon, the presiding minister over my sister's funeral and another minister stopped by the hospital to see Daddy before going on to the funeral. They told me if I chose to go to Dorothy's funeral, either of them would ensure I could get right back to Daddy's bedside. My response to them was I had done all I could do for Dorothy and that I was at the moment where I was supposed to be.

One of them asked me for Daddy's favorite biblical passage. "Your favorite biblical verse is St. John 14:1-4, isn't it Daddy?" I asked as I rubbed his forehead and held his hand. The minister began to read the passage:

"Let not [don't allow] your heart be troubled; you believe in God, believe also in Me. In My Father's house are many mansions; if it were not so, I would have told you. I go to prepare a place for you. And if I go and prepare a place for you, I will come again and receive you to Myself; that where I am, there you may be also. And where I go you know, and the way you know." [1]

Daddy reacted by opening his eyes and making muzzled sounds. I watched Daddy as the young minister completed the passage, and then said, "Daddy, I love you." Even though Daddy had an oxygen mask, he responded, "I love you, too!" I was so tickled because I could hear and understand him very well. I said it again and he responded the same. I was even more convinced that I was in the right place. The two young men left me there in order to attend my sister's funeral.

---

[1] Holy Bible: The New King James Version. 2000 (St John 14:1-4)

Dorothy's funeral was to begin at 11:00 a.m. and I was very consciously watching the clock as I talked, prayed, held my father's hand and rubbed his head. Daddy's breathing changed to a gurgling sound at 10:55 a.m. Within moments the nurses ascended quietly but quickly into the room. As I held my fingers on Daddy's hand to feel his pulse, I said to the nurses, "his breathing has changed." One nodded her head, but she would not look at me and she held her mouth tightly. I took a deep breath, smiled, and I said to my father:

"Daddy, thank you!! Thank you for being my mother's husband. Thank you for loving your children." As I called each by name, I thanked him on our behalf – all twelve of us – and told him that his wife and children truly love him. I thanked Daddy for introducing each of us to Jesus Christ, the Father, and for laying a strong spiritual foundation in his household. "We willingly release you into the arms of Jesus and we are so grateful that He loaned you to us. Go on, Daddy, and be at rest. Your life has been a sermon before me. I will love you forever, Daddy, and I know that I will see you again."

At 11:06 a.m., I heard my father take his last breath, but I could not cry. I smiled and thanked God in my heart for allowing me to be with him. What I had gained by obeying the leading of the Holy Spirit was more powerful than any pain I felt. I was immersed with gratefulness. During one of the most pivotal moments of my life, I learned the splendor of seeing circumstances through "God-colored" glasses. I felt so honored and pleased to salute my father as one does to a soldier being honorably discharged from a long-term location to an assignment in a far away land. The impact that this soldier had on my life made me stand at attention, wish him well and say good bye with great anticipation that one day we would see each other again. I knew that he would be safe in his transition.

Suddenly I realized that a nurse was crying uncontrollably and another had begun to pray aloud. In this moment I felt grace and peace as we all abided in the Shadow of the Greatness of Almighty God. He commanded one of His ambassadors to return to His native land. Daddy did not *leave* home - he *went* home.

For this moment, the decision to obey and be at my father's bedside rather than at my sister's funeral, I will be forever humbled and grateful. I am so thankful that I have dwelled in the secret place of the Most High and that I believe His Word and His promises. How else can anyone be at peace, especially with the adversities that life brings? I thank God for His shadow that covers us even as we walk "in the valley of the shadow of death." Surely goodness and mercy shall follow us as we walk in the light and truth of His Word. I view death as life after life because we are soldiers transitioning from this life to eternal life. After successfully completing a transitory mission on earth, we are promoted to greater responsibilities in an exclusive homeland called heaven. Daddy was there to celebrate my birthday into provisional life and I was there to celebrate his birthday into everlasting life.

Linda F. Delaney is a sought-after speaker, trainer, and workshop facilitator. She is a Christian writer and the author of two books. She is the President of PMA World, LLC (Training & Personal Development) and LFD Consulting, LLC (Business Management & Evaluation) that provides services to churches, other nonprofits, government agencies, as well as business and corporate clients.

Contact Linda at: www.lindafdelaney.com

Email: linda2inspire@earthlink.net

Faith Brought Me Through The Storm
By: Gail M. Butler

On August 28, 2005 my life changed forever. Born and raised in New Orleans one becomes a creature of habits with seasonal routines. Every year, citizens of New Orleans plan ahead for activities such as Mardi Gras, Essence Music Festival, Jazz Heritage Festival and the possibility of evacuation from our homes because of hurricanes. However, no one had planned for the events that took place in 2005.

Several tropical storms brewed and were classified as hurricanes but not bad enough to cause evacuation. But on a day when the sky was beautiful and all seemed peaceful, a bulletin appeared on the television, announcing a mandatory evacuation by Mayor Ray Nagin, for the City of New Orleans.

For a moment, I stared at the television, not sure if this was correct. Then my phone rang, it was my niece inviting me to travel with her family as they headed to Arkansas. "Arkansas?" I questioned, caught off guard. I'm not sure why I didn't accept, I did believe that a hurricane was on the way to New Orleans. The day before, I had gone to the grocery store and stocked up on necessities just in case there was a power outage.

My niece informed me that most of my family had already begun the process of evacuation and someone really needed to convince my mother/her grandmother to leave her home; because everyone was leaving and she would be left alone and in danger. In the past, whenever a hurricane threatened, my family would book a couple of rooms at one of the downtown hotels. We would stay there until the storm passed; even without my mother who refused to seek shelter other than the comfort of her home. One family member always managed to leave the hotel and stay with her until the hurricane passed; but no one would be able to stay with my mother this time, because everyone was in route to leave New Orleans.

So taken by all this, I spoke to my son, and related to him what was going on. He was aware and appeared worried and very concerned. "Mom," he said, "this doesn't look good. I've been watching the news, we have to leave now, this is not like the last hurricanes." My thoughts became so intense, fear gripped me and I immediately placed a call to my mother, with a serious voice, I instructed her to pack 3 days clothing because we were all leaving and she would not be staying in her house or in this city alone. I was astonished when my mother simply said, "Ok, I'll be ready." Only God could have created that swift change and decision within her. Stunned, yet very pleased that I did not have to fight with my mother, I smiled as I informed my son of his grandmother's response.

My son said, "I'm totally shocked, mom, are you sure it was my grandma?"

I laughed with my son as we quickly packed and searched for my emergency money. Then my son and I raced to mom's house and discovered my nephew and his family were there and ready to leave as well. Minutes after my call, she received a call from my nephew. He, and his family decided to go and stay with her, because of past decisions they figured she was going to be alone. But praise be to God, we all left town together. After driving several miles, we finally found a gas station still open but with very long lines. We filled our gas tanks and headed west. Gas was limited; most businesses had begun the process of closure for the mandatory evacuation.

Communication was also limited, as other family and friends were in route in various directions. Contra flow had begun (this is a procedure that becomes active during emergencies causing lane reversal to accommodate the excessive vehicles that travel in the same direction. East and west of the highway will now all travel in the same direction and you are not allowed to exit off the interstate until you have reached a certain distance that is determine by the highway authorities.) Everyone who was caught up in contra flow was frustrated or simply tired and worn out just hoping to get to their destination. We were on Interstate I-10 for over 12 hours in the contra flow madness. Finally we were able to exit off of I-10 in search of a place to sleep when we found a hotel that had available rooms. Even though we were on the road more than 12 hours, we'd only traveled 2 hours from New Orleans. Tired and exhausted, we crashed in our hotel rooms while the hurricane passed in the early morning hours.

The next morning everyone thought we had made it through another storm with high hopes of returning home. During the night the hotel had lost all power, therefore, individuals with portable radios and televisions were very much sought after; their devices were our only source of receiving information. As they shared all the shocking news regarding the devastation in our city, everyone became motionless, speechless, hurt and very scared. The familiar three-day run and return home had come to an end. Our world filled with darkness with no vision of ever returning home. Since that day, our lives became uncertain and frightening; we prayed and prayed, while others cried.

Our cell phones no longer worked, text messages through our cell phones became our only means of communication. There were many times though that text messages wouldn't go through, even if you text someone's phone in the room with you.

By the 3rd day, panic and frustration were evident amongst the hotel owners and the people. They wanted their hotel "back", because their rooms were booked before the Katrina disaster. But the people had no place to go. The hotel had begun their process to eliminate the guests when they brought in the sheriff and fire departments. That night, many people were forced to sleep in their cars. This caused panic to develop amongst the rest of us. We were all unsure where we would go or what would become of us.

My mom looked fragile and so confused, At times I wondered if she felt that had she not left the comfort of her home, things would have been much better for her. I gathered my composure, because I could not display fear and doubts. I informed everyone that I would go get our breakfast, only because I really needed to get away and think things through. I exited my hotel room to seek solace in my car, and to think of a plan that would allow us shelter at least for tonight. Praying, I asked God, "What am I to do, for I am lost, Father, this is too big for me. I don't want the hotel owners to throw us out into the street."

Thoughts of finding shelter for my mother had intensified. During my drive in search of breakfast, I found a place with a drive through, I placed our breakfast order and then was told by the worker my bill was completely covered by the customer before me. The lady assumed I was a victim of the Katrina disaster based on my Louisiana license plate and wanted to help. So numb, not grasping the conversation, I proceed to pay for our meals, but the worker at the drive through window stared at me with confusion, then she told me that my bills was covered again, and it hit me, and at the moment, I then realized that my appearance showed the pain that was in my heart and my troubled mind. I was not ready for this, it was too big for me, but I knew I had to get it together. I accepted the act of kindness with a thank you, and I headed back to the hotel. The situation at the hotel was growing out of control and my phone kept going off with a 911 text but I could not reply.

After returning back to the hotel, my phone continued to receive the urgent 911 phone text. Feeling panic, fearing bad news might be coming regarding my sister whose is ventilator depended and tube feed with ALS - Amyotrophic Lateral Sclerosis, also known as Lou Gehrig's Disease. She was institutionalized in a nursing facility in New Orleans. My sister has no vocal or mobile communicating skills; it was lost due to the disease, therefore she would not be able to communicate to the doctors and nurses on how to contact her family. We knew she wasn't at the nursing home. The day before, I had talked with her nurse and they assure us she would be transported to the assigned hospital. Because of her medical condition and the guidelines, anytime a storm threatened, she had to be transported to a hospital. Unfortunately, due to the flood, most, if not all the hospitals in New Orleans was affected.

Too afraid for my mom to receive any more bad information, I left the hotel room in search of a pay telephone so that I could find out who sent me the text and what this urgency was all about.

After driving around several miles in search of a working pay phone, it seemed every pay phone I tried was out of order; some even took my quarters which I had a limited amount of. While searching for a working phone, I received several text messages from my son asking my whereabouts because I was needed back at the hotel. I decided to drive just a little further because I needed to find out about this 911 text phone call. Between the 911 phone call and the text messages from my son, I couldn't concentrate; by now, my mind was in a tailspin. I knew I should have returned to the hotel but I needed to find out about this 911 call. I don't even know how far I traveled before I spotted another pay phone. My heart began to race as I quickly drove up to it, jumped out my car, still praying, *Lord please let this be a working phone.* Glory to God, the phone worked and the 911 call was an invitation from the family where other members of my family had evacuated to in Katy, Texas. They wanted me to bring the rest of my family to their home also.

When I got back to the hotel I discovered that the hotel management had given hourly notices to some of the guest concerning their checkout time (meaning, they had to check out that day). The management informed me that I had the option to stay additional days, but I must pay in full for those days up front and should I leave sooner, they would not refund my money. Hallelujah, thank you Jesus for having me out in search of that pay phone. I raced to the room my family was in and relayed the joyful message concerning the family in Katy, Texas to everyone. Then I became overwhelmed with joy, I cried uncontrollably because my prayers had truly been answered. This was the first time since this whole ordeal began that I let my family witness my vulnerability. I was no longer in control. I accepted that fact with humility. I then realized, I was never the one in charge, God was and has been and is still in control.

The next day, we checked out the hotel and made our way to Katy, Texas. We were happy to have somewhere to go, but we were still uncertain. Once we reached the family who graciously invited us to join our other family members, we felt our first moment of peace since this nightmare began. Over 20 plus people found a safe and loving haven in Minister Edwards home. They opened their doors, floors and hearts to us all. We slept in our sleeping bags, air mattresses, on the sofa, and chairs, it didn't matter; we were together.

Still in search of other family members, day after day, we suffered a myriad of emotions as we watched the news. The nursing home where my sister was institutionalized had gone completely under, and we knew that no one could have survived. We made many calls while looking at the TV screen with hopes of information for locating my sister as well as other family members. My other sister worked at a hospital in New Orleans.

74

She had agreed to stay on her job and to assist however possible once she knew her family had evacuated, yet still other family members had not been located. After weeks on the phone and the internet, we finally located my sister with ALS through Red Cross. She was air lifted to a hospital further west of New Orleans. Even though we were not able to speak to her, they assure us she would be taken care of.

***

Standing in long lines and visiting the Texas Reliant Center became our daily routine, in order to obtain assistance from the government, and in search of other family members. We found several family members and friends that were snatched out of the raging waters or rescued from their homes. Hypnotized by the news, we saw our once comfortable homes washed away as the water rose. We witnessed family and friends on the TV trying to survive the madness at the Superdome and the Convention Center. We saw bodies floating, and to make matters worst, hurricane Rita developed and we assumed that she would finish what Katrina started. Hours turned into days, days into weeks before we could even return home to assess the damage from the two hurricanes.

Once we were given the okay to enter our beloved New Orleans, we headed home. Minister Edwards prayed a powerful prayer for our safe return. The Texas/Louisiana border, from Texas to New Orleans was lined with numerous army vehicles. The drive home felt as if we'd been placed in the middle of a combat zone. This didn't feel good, and the ride was long and the drive was hard. We were so terrified of this whole ordeal being displayed before us, we drove in silence.

Knowing our visit would only be temporary didn't lessen the fears. As we entered into the surrounding parishes before New Orleans, we had to be cleared by the service men by showing our Identification and proof of residence or we would not be allow in New Orleans. At 6am the sun had just begun to rise, but no one noticed the darkness before the sun rose, because the military was shinning giant spotlights on the interstate at the check point. This was all too scary, a familiar scene out of "White Nights".

Along the way, before reaching the city of New Orleans, we could see that the surrounding parishes had sustained major damage. Yet, this was not enough to prepare us for what we found. Trees and power lines were down, houses moved completely from their foundation, now resting blocks away. There were exposed dead animals with gnats every where and the smell of death in the air nearly choked us.

Once inside the city and headed toward my community, we saw abandoned cars turned over, trees and debris blocked our path as we were forced to maneuver to reach our destination. As we approached my home, the appearance and the smell seemed like something staged for a horror movie. We suited up with our face masks, bodysuits, head protectors, rubber knee high boots and rubber gloves. None of the doors were accessible; they were blocked by mold infected furniture that had floated away from its rightful place.

Once we created an entrance, by crashing and climbing in a window, we discovered it was all for nothing. Even with face mask protectors, it didn't completely block the horrible smell, so horrible it caused us to gag. As I tried to survey the damage, I finally realized everything I owned, that took years to acquire had been destroyed. Water reached over 10 feet in my community, evident by the water stains and lines on and around the ceiling and the mold all along the walls. It gave my house the appearance of an unattractive and very frightening mirage. It smelled horrible and the mud in my house was so deep that it was hard to maneuver. Everything was covered in mud and contaminated; nothing was salvageable. The refrigerator floated and made its way to the living room entrance door. The kitchen cabinets and breakfast counter collapsed and all the furniture was upside down all atop of each other, while some floated to other areas of the house. This was all too much. I broke down and cried for my losses and the ruin of my city and community. When I was all cried out, we disrobed of all our protective gear, started up the car and headed back once again in silence, making the decision to relocate to what I now call home...Katy, Texas.

At the point when I felt nothing else could go wrong I received a directive from my employer requesting all employees to return to work. *How could this be*? I wondered. I was not ready; I had no place to live in New Orleans. How could such a directive be made? Do they know what has happened to the city and the people of New Orleans? Everyone was afraid for my return to New Orleans and asked me not to go back to work, but I knew I had to go.

I only had a few days to prepare for my return. I was frustrated, and confused because I had no place to live. I placed a call to FEMA for a trailer at one of the trailer sites, then I placed a call to a friend of mine. She had already returned to her home and job. Her apartment was located on the west bank, her community had not been damage by the flood, but did sustain some wind and rain damage from the hurricane. She said I could stay with her during my transition period. I then began to make plans for my return to New Orleans. Visions of my last visit prompted fear and frustration. Upon my arrival, I was so frustrated, in a panic and full of fear that I became ill and had to seek medical treatment.

My friend had only one bedroom so I used the sofa bed in her living room as my sleeping quarters. Springs on a soft bed is designed for temporary sleeping only. I soon discovered, after a couple of weeks, my body ached each and every morning as I rose to prepare for work. My movement was patterned after my aging mother. One morning I could not get out of the bed, because it ached so badly. I then knew I had to make a change regarding my sleeping quarters. I once again put my sleeping bag on the floor. I slept each and every night on the floor in my sleeping bag while in New Orleans for six months until an apartment unit became available. Throughout this time I continued to contact FEMA, but still no trailer was available. Now I drive/fly monthly to Texas to be with my family.

Although I have a job and a place to live, the aftermath of Katrina caused me to be diagnosed with depression, I've suffered from anxiety and have been totally stressed out. But through it all I still have to say, I am truly Blessed. He's blessed me moreover than before. Unfortunately some family and friends didn't survive this ordeal. But because of God's Grace and Mercy most did. We're scattered across state lines, some have returned to New Orleans, while others are making a new beginning away from our beloved New Orleans. No matter the distance, we have Jesus as our Savior. "[For] I sought the LORD, and he answered me; he delivered me from all my fears" psalm 34:4.

Gail M. Butler, a native of New Orleans, member of the Little Zion Baptist Church, and a single mother who survived the Hurricane Katrina disaster and the raging flood waters of 2005. Her story is dedicated to the Edwards who sheltered, fed and loved her family, which kept them together when their world appeared shattered. Gail is currently employed with the Louisiana State Government and is fast approaching retirement status.

Contact Gail at: www.mytestimony2005.com email:

gailbutler2005@yahoo.com

The Second Time Around
By: Arnita Fields

Have you ever blamed someone for a mess that you had gotten yourself into? Or have you ever been caught off guard and ill prepared for your seasons of testing? Has anyone ever done anything to harm you and God opened your eyes so you could see that there was a silver lining? No matter what you may be going through or experiencing at this very moment, know that someone truly cares about you. His love is so strong and so deep for you, that the oceans would not even be deep enough to contain the love that's stored up for you. God is love, and He has made a way of escape out of every test or trail. Psalms 48:14 says, "For this God is our God forever and ever; He will be our guide even unto death." The Holy Spirit is there to guide us out. All we have to do is humble ourselves and allow the spirit of God to direct our footsteps.

Now let me share with you how God gave me a way of escape out of adultery, bitterness, and a spirit of fear. I really did not know that I had been selected to become a target of the enemy in 1999, but none the less I was. In fact I did not see myself as a serious threat, honestly. I loved God and strived to serve Him as best as I could, but unknown to me, God had greater plans for my life and there were some generational curses in my family line that I had to face. If I had any previous insight as to what I was about to go through, I would have passed this assignment up without blinking, not realizing that I would have forfeited my blessing in the end.

Falling in love with my husband Anthony came easy, much to my surprise. He was really down to earth, as well as a real quiet type. We were opposites in so many ways, but so alike in many others. We went together like peanut butter and jelly (both of our

79

favorite sandwiches). Two different textures, but tasted good when mixed together. I knew that when we got married we would have some of the normal potholes that new married couples fall into, but as it turned out we had some holes as large as the Grand Canyon to deal with. These holes were not something that God did not know about, but they were things that God was openly exposing by the light of His spirit.

I can't remember the exact date or time when the trouble began, but I noticed that I became more irritable by the day. Attitudes and mood swings were quite frequent for me. I truly see now that I was a ticking bomb waiting to explode. I had no idea that I had so much bitterness bottled up on the inside. With my husband being the quiet type, our fights were basically one sided. I was always the one who wanted to have the absolute final word.

My purging by God had already begun and I did not even understand what was taking place, I just knew that I was not happy about where I was in my life at that moment. My husband and I had talked about our relationship with the Lord on so many occasions and we always took the time out to read our bible together. We really tried hard to make it work, but something was truly missing. As the year 2000 approached, we began to grow apart in our hearts, but we still decided that we would keep trying to work at our marriage. I knew in my own heart that Anthony was the man that I was to be with, but we needed some help. Who could we trust, who could we confide in without being judged at the same time? The sand in the hour glass finally ran out for us one evening in 2000 when I came home from work to a letter from my husband wanting out of our marriage. In the letter he stated that it was him and not me (he was much too generous with the kind words). He said that he felt I deserved a better man than he. I was hurt by this because I felt that we had begun to talk openly about what was wrong in our relationship. Since he made the decision to go, I had to make some decisions about my future as well. Should we divorce?

All while I was dealing with my broken marriage, I was also dealing with sickness in my body and also a crushed and wounded spirit that came as a result of spiritual abuse that both my husband and I endured at a ministry we had attended. God, what's really up? What am I supposed to do now? These were valid questions that I asked as I saw my little world come crashing to my feet.

The instruction that I received in my spirit after a 7 day cleansing fast, was both direct and to the point. I was lead to the book of Genesis, chapter 12 verses 1-3 where Abram was asked to leave his father's country and go to a place that God would show him. In other words, if I was going to become who God really wanted me to become, I had to get out of Memphis and fast. In fact I was given a deadline of what day I was supposed to be gone from the city. When I first heard about Nashville, I fought it with all of my heart. I had planned to go to TSU in 1984 after graduating from high school but opted for a Wisconsin school instead. Now I was really going to Nashville. Could this all be a part of God's plan?

Before I even went to check out Nashville, God had already begun to heal me of many hurts and pains from before my marriage. I truly was a broken woman, more than I even realized. I spent the first few nights crying myself to sleep, while staying in a motel room, only to get up the next day, paint my face and get dressed for work. I kept up this front until the weight of the mask began to wear too heavy on me. My husband and I talked from time to time, but he too had become bitter. Some days I thought he and I both were crazy, he for walking away and me for trying to love him. In the midst of all of this madness, I found a place of worship in Nashville that helped me to forget about my mess at least for a few hours each Sunday.

When I walked into my new church home in Nashville, TN I felt connected and truly a part of something big. There was warmth there that I had not felt anywhere before. I felt as though God Himself had wrapped me in His strong loving arms and hid me. As I listened to the word and purchased the tapes to play at home, I began to loosen up and realize that everything I'd gone through was all part of a strategic plan to get me closer to God's purpose in my life. Although the enemy meant it for harm, God was turning something bad into something for the good of the kingdom. The false walls had to come down, so the Holy Spirit could gain entry. This is when my true healing began.

Soon the calls between my husband and I came to a slow crawl. The majority of my contact with him came through his siblings, who at times treated me harshly. With that kind of feedback from my in-laws, it only added fuel to the fire and tempted me to just cut the whole family off and cement the door shut behind me. I really did not have much support from my family either. Some days I felt alone in the world, while trying to crawl out of the mud I felt locked into. To be totally honest, I began to not really trust anyone with what I was going through because they viewed me as the victim, when they truly did not have all of the facts. If only they knew the whole story.

As time went on my husband and I communicated back and forth that we were divorcing. One day I got tired of hearing the word divorce, so I told him to go for it. Just send me the papers and we'll both be free. If a person is going to threaten me, they should follow through with what they say they are going to do. I just wanted out even though I knew in my heart that I was not to divorce my husband. God had plans to revive the dry and brittle bones in both of our lives and God Himself was going to breathe on us and revive our wearied souls.

The time had finally come when I was allowed to come back to Memphis and visit my husband. It had been three long years of separation and I had become a born again virgin. This was how I should have really been presented to my husband before marriage in the first place, a woman whole who was healed.

When I first laid eyes on my husband during our first meeting, he looked worn out in the spirit. I could see him struggling against the very one who had reached out to save him from the raging floods. God was calling his name, but my husband was not responding. Although this visit was accompanied by a bit of drama before our meeting, I knew I had an assignment to complete before going back to Nashville. The enemy was not going to stop me no matter what. After our meeting in Memphis, my husband became real nervous and antsy. It was as if he had turned into another person.

I tell you the time after our meeting set the stage for my fall from grace. Although In the past I was not able to prove that my husband had another woman, I knew when I left Memphis that he had been in a relationship with a woman for the past 3 years.

He told me during my visit that he still loved me. Um, yeah right. It's a thin line between love and hate. Although he never confessed to me directly that he was with the woman whom I'll call Lisa, I did have a opportunity to call her home and ask her to put my husband on the phone; which she did. I had gotten her phone number from one of my husband's relatives. I was not to call her when I got the phone number, but you know; I could not just let that number burn a hole in my purse! When I had the urge to call my husband to talk about our upcoming divorce, I would just call to Lisa's house in Memphis and ask to speak to my husband and she would just hand him the phone. She made mention to me that she thought that my husband and I were already divorced when they met 3 years earlier, I told her no, I was still his wife.

I went back to Nashville, wondering what in the world was I thinking. I made an appointment to see a divorce lawyer that same week. It fell through because the lawyer forgot our appointment. Then I made another appointment that did not work out either. Lord, I'm trying, what's the real deal here? You want me to love a man that does not want to be loved? Yes, was the reply I heard. Yes, you love him as I have loved you.

One day I allowed doubt to lead me to fall from grace. I had teased my husband by calling him David the adulterer not showing any compassion at all. But when I let a male associate come to watch a movie at my apartment, I let him into my personal space and ended up committing the very act of adultery that I had judged my husband on previously. How could I have let that happen? Something I said that I would never do? What had gotten into me? I was angry with myself because I let my guard down. I tried to justify my actions. Well we're separated anyway. I had to get out of this mess and fast.

The man I had laid with began to threaten me when I told him it was over between us. He said that he was going to tell people that he knew at my church what happened between us. I was petrified. He said my husband gave me away, so I should go on. I went to this man, whom I'll call Robert and told him that I did not care what he did or who he told, I was not going to see him anymore. He got mad and would follow me to my job. One day I walked into the lobby and there he was delivering flowers for someone (he did deliveries for a florist); I nearly passed out with fear. One day while sitting at my desk a phone call was transferred from the front desk. I answered and wouldn't you know it? It was Robert. Anger began to rise up in me and I said in a hushed tone as not to let my fellow cube mates overhear me, "What do you want? It's been months why are you still bothering me?" He said that he missed me. I told him there was nothing to miss, so get lost. He said, so you must be back with your husband? Out of spite I said yes, I am. He then said that he wanted to date the receptionist anyway and wanted to know what I could tell him about her. How dare he? I hung the phone up in his face. I did not hear from him again until a few weeks later when he called my cell phone. I called him back and told him my number would be changed the very next day. I have not heard from him since.

Things had gotten crazy for a bit but the most hurtful thing was the fact that my relationship with God had been jeopardized. I prayed and cried, prayed and cried. I wrote poetry and studied my word. I was hurting bad because I had hurt God. Lord, how could I fall, and for a man that I was not even attracted to?

My second and final act of adultery occurred a few months later. This time it was the brother-in-law of a close friend. I was attracted to his body, which was not normally what I looked for in a man. When he walked me to my front door after giving me a ride home from the grocery store, he had leaned in and stole a kiss. I stood in my door shocked and speechless. He said that he desired me for a while, but did not know if I was going back to my husband. We then had a one night stand. I broke it off the next day when I found out that he was married and had a child.

What I was seeing and what I was experiencing was an answer to a question I had asked God concerning my husband. I wanted to know how he could violate our marriage   and sleep at night. I always wondered what people were thinking when they cheated on their spouses. I was curious as to why they could not just get out of their mess and go home and get things right with their spouses. Now I knew it was not as easy as people thought it should be. It takes time to forgive and to be forgiven. There is a process of healing and restoration, and a process of sanctification that follows.

I would say that the whole experience humbled me to the ground. But then I was led in my spirit to apologize to my husband. It had been seven months since our first meeting, and things had been real civil between us, as we talked on the phone weekly. We had discussed getting back together and decided that we both never really wanted a divorce, but we were trying to manipulate each other to get our own way. How sad, but true. When we met for a weekend to discuss our future, I confessed my sin of adultery to my husband. I watched his expression as I told him the news. I will say he looked truly hurt and shocked all at the same time. He told me that he thought that I would never cheat on him. I told him, that I found out that just because I was saved by grace, I was not excluded from falling to the lust of the flesh. I was a woman who turned to another man instead of turning to God when I felt slighted by my husband.

Those needing forgiveness have to be humble enough to receive it, even when they feel they don't really deserve it at that time. Forgiveness is definitely not an option. It is a requirement as stated in Matthew 18:21-35. The same forgiveness that I was shown by God after committing adultery not once, but twice was the same way I was to have treated my husband when I found out about his trespass. Sin is sin and it did not matter what happened in the past. We both had violated our marriage vows, so the case was closed on the whole matter.

We ended up talking for hours into the early morning. Since I had known my husband, I had never heard him talk so long. I was asked to just listen as he poured out his heart as to why he left and why he wanted to come back. He told me that he never stopped loving me, but felt hurt when I left the city. He said that he always knew that I was his wife, but he needed to get things out of his life that he said he did not even know he had on the inside of himself.

We then made a pact to be more open, and I promised to listen before I spoke what was on my mind. God was at that very moment salvaging a marriage and stopping the spirit of divorce that had loomed in my family line for years. My husband was learning what real love felt like, the kind of love that God pours into a wife for her husband and vice versa. You know, it's the purified kind of love. I too had also learned what it felt like to be loved. God had shown me how by the way He loved me throughout all of my mistakes and errors. God loved me unconditionally and I was able to love myself as well as my husband in that same way too.

It's been three years and three months since our third and final meeting. Since that time God has taken us from faith to faith in our relationship. We did experience some setbacks at the beginning, when I found myself trying to control the direction of our marriage. But as always, the Holy Spirit tugged at me and said, "let your husband lead, let him be the man. I have him. He knows how to hear from me just like you do. Let God have His way, it's going to be okay." And you know what? God has been having His way.

We have a beautiful marriage and a wonderful relationship. We laugh and share our feelings now. We don't curse and hide our emotions on the inside anymore. We both have become more sensitive to the needs of each other. Our God has restored His divine order in our home, and He can restore order in your home too. Won't you let Him into your heart today? Give God a try and allow the power of His wonderful presence to heal and restore you. It does not matter what you have been caught up in, God is a mighty deliverer. There is a way of escape. If He can deliver me, He'll do the same for you too. Trust Him and allow faith in God to see you through.

Minister Arnita L. Fields is a native of Milwaukee, Wisconsin. She was born the 3rd of six children. She attended John Marshall High school and also UW Whitewater in Wisconsin, where she majored in Broadcast Communications. Arnita's writing experience started when she was in grade school, but her love for poetry was reborn in 1998, when she took a Literature class at State Tech in Memphis, TN. Her writing credits include 2 books of poetry to date.

Contact Minister Arnita at: email: arnitafields@yahoo.com

That Kind of Man: A Tribute to My Father
By: Vicki Austin

The day my father was diagnosed with head and neck cancer, Is one I will never forget. My mother and I had just shared a mother-daughter night out the Saturday before he was to go into the hospital for a biopsy. A big Danny Glover and Mel Gibson fan, Mom and I laughed and held on to the theater seats as we ran, jumped and brought the bad guys to justice while watching "Lethal Weapon". Afterwards we had dinner, chatted and then parted ways. At about 1:00 am my phone rang. I knew it would probably not be good news. I picked up the phone, and mom told me she was experiencing chest pain.

I dressed quickly, grabbed my young son, bundled him up and put him in the car. When I arrived at my childhood home, mom was ready to go. She looked weak and had difficulty breathing. I wondered why my dad wasn't taking her to the hospital, but didn't ask. Once in the ER, they stabilized her. Hooking her up to monitors and inserting IV tubing into her arm and oxygen into her nostrils. While my son lay sleeping, I called my siblings to let them know our whereabouts. They said they would be on the way soon.

After all the tests were completed, the Doctor came and explained to us that mother had a blockage in a coronary artery and it needed to be removed. By 8:00 am now Sunday, they had her in surgery, performing the procedure on her.

The Doctor returned and let us all know that she was fine and would be sent to a unit where she would be monitored for a couple of days. It seemed strange to me at that point that my dad still had not made it to the hospital. When I called, he inquired in specific detail about mom with deep concern and then we hung up. I didn't quite dismiss his unusual action, but instead I tried to focus on moms needs. She had a moment there in the Intensive Care Unit that shook us all. They tried to remove the bandage from her femoral site and blood came gushing up. Extreme pressure was applied and they were able to stabilize her once again before her Blood pressure dipped too low.

After conversing over mom as she dozed in and out of sleep, we three decided that my sister would take my dad to get his biopsy since she worked as an RN at the hospital he had to get the test done at. My brother and I who worked at the hospital my mother was presently in, so we stayed with mom and await my sister's call with news on my father as she got it. On Monday, my sister took dad into admissions and they proceeded to prep him. My sister waited alone.

My mother, around that same time was sitting in a chair by the sink in her nightgown; the nurse and I were trying to help her freshen up so she could hopefully be dismissed later that morning. While sitting there, mom had a feeling of faintness and was put back to bed, now slimming the chance that she would be dismissed later that day. As the Doctor and nurse talked, it became clear that she wouldn't be released until tomorrow or the day after. When I told the nurse my dad was in surgery at that moment, she mused that perhaps mom felt my dad's pain; that soul connections such as my Mom and Dad's are common in couples who had been married as long as they had. Finally, with mom chiding me, I left the unit and I went home to get some rest.

Awaiting a call from my sister regarding my father's outcome, I lay there trying to drift into a restful sleep. The phone rang after several hours and my sister sounded utterly distraught.

My sister cried softly as she told me dad had come out of the surgery with a tracheal tube in his throat and bandages everywhere as well as markings on his face. Although we handle patients in that shape every day, it isn't the same when you see a loved one in that type of distress. The surgeons confirmed that our father did have a large tumor on the back of his tongue (which they removed) and some cancer cells were found in his throat. I almost dropped the phone but held on tight for the rest of the report my sister was giving me. I knew then why my dad had not come to the hospital the day before. He was indeed weak and very sick.

We didn't know at the time that he and my mom had talked to ENT specialists who had given him a probable diagnosis. My parents had not wanted to worry us until all the test results came back. No one expected however, for mom to be in crises and that dad would wake up different from when he went under anesthesia.

When I called my mother and told her what had happened, she said to me. "God knows best. If I had been there I probably would have had a heart attack when they rolled him out on that stretcher," As close as they were, and as many years as they had been cleaving to one another I didn't doubt what she said. I then began running between hospitals. Praying for the best. Praying for God to strengthen us all through this time.

On Tuesday morning they finally released mom and the first place we went was to see my dad. I had seen dad the day before and the unexpected encounter all but brought me to my knees. I tried to prepare mom as best I could. Daddy couldn't talk, but he wanted to so bad. When he saw mother, he kept trying to verbalize but the swelling around the trachea wouldn't allow him. In his frustration he was gesturing for a pen and paper.

Mom was attentive to dad's every need. As we watched her care for her husband until he was released from the hospital. When my father returned home he never once asked "why me?" Not aloud anyway. Never once did he complain about pain. He could be heard praying "Lord ease my pain so I can bear it," my mother started a routine of giving him prescribed pain medication to make sure he had it, otherwise he would not ask. The tracheal and the Nasogastric tube he had to wear in order to continue his nourishment didn't stop him. He was stoic just as he had always

90

been. Stern, firm, self assured in himself as a man and grounded in his faith.

He sported that nasogastric (Dobbhoff) tube everywhere he went without shame; to the store, visiting friends, going to church. The hardest thing for my dad to do at that time was to retire from his civilian job as a security guard at Vencor Hospital. He liked it there. He was a calm and quiet man, but he loved witnessing to the patients. My dad had served this country 24 years of his life. He was a decorated Air Force man. But his greatest role, he'd often say, was his service to God and his God given wisdom, health and divine providence.

He had done his 20 plus years in the USAF as a communications specialist. Retired from military life and again retired from civil service in almost the same capacity. The security job had kept him busy and allowed him to greet, meet and make friends. He touched really sick people as he made his rounds.

I often describe my father as a man whom without talking loud or much, was always saying something. His silence spoke to you. Reeled you in; left you wanting to ask, "A penny for your thoughts dad?"

He had such great character. A man from the old school. He was honest and proud of where he came from. He was a great provider. He cherished our mother and had no problems displaying that. He was hard working, and witty. The man ate the strangest combinations of food: such as bananas and peanut butter sandwiches, mayonnaise and tomato sandwiches, which he often tried to blame on his poor childhood. A handsome Alabama native who had seen the ravages of racism, but never let it turn him into something bitter. He was trusting in others (He actually believed people could still sleep with their doors unlocked until about the mid eighties) and generous to a fault. He served God as he was taught by a mother and father who bore and raised fifteen children. My dad, the second oldest, served this country and was a man of

91

substance when it came to his intelligence, integrity and his devotion.

Cancer, chemotherapy, nor radiation, changed daddy. Not the essence of who he was as a man. He never lost his pretty salt and pepper gray hair with the treatments. He was at peace with the issues of living and dying. He was calm and he evoked that calm spirit in others. I remember one of his nurses telling me, that when my father came into the office, she would always come to sit next to him, after a harried day; sitting next to him would bring her a sense of relaxation and ease her tension. He never stopped smiling through his pain. He could still crack a mean joke or laugh at something he found humorous.

As the hospitalizations became more frequent and his physical body became a little more frail, I would carry with me the rest of my life the things he said in a family Round Table meeting we had. Daddy's last.

He emphasized the importance of family, and how we have to love one another, even when we become most unlovable. That people in our lives would come and go but the kinship and camaraderie of family endures.

He made us write down exactly what his wishes were for his service. My sister wrote, my brother choked back tears, I held dad's large hand in my own petite one and mother sobbed. He knew she was not ready for him to go. But knew he would be going anyway.

I continued to watch my mother and father as the days passed. Their relationship was strong; as tightly woven as an intricately stitched blanket made by hand and homemade love. Her loving hands would crush his pills, change his feeding tube, caress his brow or stroke his arms and legs as she lotioned him after baths. The closeness shone through in the little looks that passed between them. It was also evident in the gestures she made, the tenderness in the touch as she cared for him, not allowing the home health

92

team the opportunity to do very much for him. And Daddy was holding on to every precious moment they shared.

My father had always been big on taking family photos. He would tell us all to get dressed and meet him in the back yard. All of us clowning, making faces, posing and making silly memories that would forever be imprinted on Kodak paper and etched in our hearts. That is the way I saw daddy in his last weeks, taking mental pictures of us all, to carry along with him on his new journey.

At the time my son was eight years old, turning nine soon. He too saw the courage, the fight and the strength in his papa. I had been prayerfully preparing him for the day that would no doubt arrive. Explaining so his young mind could grasp what it meant to die. I told him where we go when this journey ends and another part of the life cycle begins. He knew the loss would hurt us, and that we would miss him. The week my father declined, hospice took him into their care. The Monday evening my dad left the home of my youth, I knew he wouldn't return. He was up on Tuesday, alert and dozing in and out of sleep. While my son was in school, I would sit by his bed and talk to him. Thanking him for being the dad he was and holding his now frail hand in mine, the way he used to hold my tiny hand as a child, when I got stitches in the ER or had a bad stomach ache; or while walking me into kindergarten on the first day of my scholastic career, the same way he held it on my wedding day. He had seemed larger than life, big, durable, a towering hero that could conquer and chase away all my fears. He still was all of that, and I had no idea what toll it would take on me to see him go.

On Friday night the nurse called me. She said daddy was restless and I asked if she could get a VCR in the room for my son; She did. We went to the Hospice center and though the room was lovely, my focus was on my father. I remember my son climbing in bed with him, reading him a bedtime story. He watched a movie and fell asleep on the extra bed. He was excited about the trip he was taking to Six Flags with friends the next day. As the night went on, I assured mom that dad was indeed restless but she should get some rest. But as darkness went on, his breathing became erratic and he kept trying to sit up, reaching toward the ceiling. I went to him and sat there on his bed, wondering if he could see me. The nurses that were coming on duty were all beginning to recognize my dad as the shifts changed.

They exclaimed, "Oh my God, he worked with us at Vencor." They went on to tell me short tales about their knowing daddy as they tenderly cared for him and explained to me what they were giving my father to ease his pain and to help dry his secretions. Sometimes they would pop in to touch his arm and ask how I was doing. At those moments, I thought about how awesome God is. That even in the last days of my father's life he had provided angels in the human form, lives he had also touched to touch him and care for him as he prepared for his home going. When his Doctor said so, I called mom and she came immediately. I could only picture her trying to get dressed alone, and wondered what must be going through her mind. Mom arrived and climbed in bed with daddy.

Family friends came and went. Daddy was slipping away. My sister arrived and the day moved on. We talked to him and touched him, loved on my dad like one can only do when the end is near.

Late in the evening, my dad seemed calmer. The nurse suggested we go out on the terrace and eat a bite. Still waiting for my brother, we reluctantly went to sit in the beautiful garden underneath a gazebo. We'd each had time with my father to tell him what was in our heart, and to tell him it was okay for him to leave us. The words my mother had spoken as I sat there in my tears feeling like a voyeur would remain with me and sustain me in lessons concerning true love and its staying power. She thanked him for the many years of life together, love, and laughter. For the hard times which only made her stronger. And she assured him that he was the love of her life and there would be no other but him. The words reverberated in my spirit as she held his hand, kissed him and told him he had taught her how to gracefully succumbed to death. She no longer feared death, and she would be there when her time came to meet him in eternity. She told him it was alright to go, assured him she would be alright. As she spoke, tears ran down my daddy's face on each side, hitting the pillow as he listened but couldn't speak. She told him she was blessed, because she knew what it meant, to really be loved!

My brother went in to say goodbye, he was teary when he joined us for a bite. Done eating, we headed back to dad's room. Mom took her vigil lying at daddy's side in bed.

We began watching a movie, but when we noticed his breathing change, we all walked to the foot of the bed and gathered in a circle. My brother, the eldest held my father's left shoulder. My sister, the middle child held my fathers left hand, I held on to my father's leg.

My mother stood beside him as she always had since the day they met and held his right hand: her rightful position not going unnoticed. We gently stroked him, each of us calmly talking and watching my father gaze toward the far left upper corner in the room. His face was serene as he slipped from our grasp to cross over into rest. He left us with so many memories. Fresh quiet tears flowed unchecked. The moment was painful yet joyous, knowing his destination and that his suffering was over.

The answers in my father's peacefulness and my mother's stillness on the day of his death set me on a path of perfected love. To love no matter what. My divorce had left me reeling and wondering where I went wrong. It had messed me up! But daddy would say, "turn it over to Jesus, baby girl." Hopefully, one day God will send me the right fit, just as he fitted mom and dad. If not, I am convinced that having seen it in them, having been born into it and being nurtured by it, will keep my heart open for whatever life brings my way. I learned many lessons from my parents as I was growing up. I cherish those lessons and try to live by them now. Before my dad's body was taken away that Saturday night, my son drove up, as the Hearst pulled in.

I picked him up and asked him how his day at Six Flags had been. "Great, we had a blast" he said.

"So did papa. Tonight he went home to be with God and his family and friends who were waiting for him. I am sure they are having a blast right now, a wonderful celebration."

Love doesn't die with those who are closest to you; it lives Just as Jesus lives in eternity. I now understand that love keeps on growing, even after the person and the acute pain from the loss is gone. Death is a part of life and we should never take God's daily gifts for granted. He called one of his best soldiers home but, I shall see daddy again!

I thank God that my parent's taught me to believe in the things I can't visibly see. To walk by faith and not by sight.

Vicki J. Austin resides in San Antonio, Texas with her 17 year old son Deondre'. Vicki has various hobbies and is involved in literary programs that aid people of all ages. She is also founder of S.W.I.F.T. Inc. A Women's Organization that gives back to the community. Contact Vicki at: email: vickiaustin22@aol.com

TROUBLE IN MY WAY
By: Vanessa Miller

CHAPTER 1

Tears of regret sprang in Kenisha's eyes as the doctor shouted, "Push!"

"No. I can't."

"You acted like a grown woman when you spread your legs to make this baby. Act like one now and push him out."

She barely knew this man in the white coat, crotched between her legs, demanding that she push her baby out of a hole that was too small for some grapefruit size head to get through. She turned to James, pleading her case. "He's too big. I can't get him out."

James wiped away the tears that trickled down his woman's ashened face. "You can do this Ke-Ke. You're a woman now. Remember that."

Smirking the doctor mumbled, "I've never met a fifteen-year old woman."

Strength from way down deep grew in Kenisha as she shifted her swollen body to look Dr. Holton in the eye. He was disrespecting her. People got cut for mess like that where she came from.

"I've been taking care of myself for more years than I can count," she told him, then stilled herself as an explosion ripped through her body. Pain so sharp and mind blowing, it made her want to travel back to the beginning of time, snatch Eve up by her nappy roots and smack the fruit juice out of her mouth.

"You okay, Ke-Ke?"

She wanted to smack James too. All his baby, baby pleases put her in this predicament. But her desire to wipe that smug, bet-you-wish-you'd-listened-to-your-mama look off Dr. Holton's face directed her energy toward her belly. Panting, as the pain subsided, she told them, "This baby is ready to meet his Mama."

"Then push," Dr. Holton said.

Grinding down, Kenisha pushed, not once, but three times, before her sweat-drenched body collapsed on the bed.

"I've got the head," Dr. Holton said, as he positioned himself to extract the shoulders. "One more push, Kenisha. Come on. You can do it."

Her insides were exploding, or were they imploding? She really didn't care what the correct term was. She was ready to throw in the towel, scream "Uncle," call for a truce, or beg this big-head baby for mercy. How on earth was she supposed to push again? She was dying. Couldn't they see that? Dr. Holton was right. The delivery room was no place for a fifteen – going on thirty-five year old girl. There, she admitted it. Now could somebody please *get this baby out*!

If she died with her baby half in, half out, everyone would know she was a fraud. She couldn't really handle life.

She thought about praying. But she hadn't done much of that since she was nine years old, sneaking out to Sunday school at the church down the street from the Arlington Courts project homes she'd aged beyond her years in. That's where she'd heard that Bible story about a woman who wanted a child more than anything. The woman promised God that if He would give her a child, she would give the baby back to Him. Another pain shot through her and she screamed, "He's Yours God, just help me through this."

The next few minutes passed like a blur. Her last push was faint, but she felt like Christmas had come, when the pain of birth subsided. Then she heard the cry of her child, and knew that God had been with her.

James moved a few strands of wet hair from her face. "You did it Ke-Ke. Our son is here."

Stretching out weary arms, she said, "Hand me my son."

The nurse had just finished cleaning the baby. She looked to Dr. Holton. He nodded his approval.

She couldn't sit up. So, when the nurse put her baby in her hands, she brought him to her lips and kissed his forehead. She and James had already picked out a name for their son. As best she could, Kenisha lifted Jamal Anthony Moore and proclaimed, "Thank You for my son, Lord. I give him back to You."

CHAPTER 2

Twenty-three and played out. Like the words of a tired old blues song, Kenisha Smalls had been strung and rung out.

"Too young to give up," she chided as she pulled herself out of bed. But when her feet hit the floor, and her knees buckled from unexplained pain, she reminded herself that she had actually lived a hundred dog years; lapping at the crumbs from underneath other folk's tables, and being kicked around by more good-for-nothings than she could count. A few years back, Kenisha thought some good would have to come into her life to even out the bad. But when James, her first baby's daddy got arrested for armed robbery, and then Terrell, her second baby's daddy got himself shot and killed trying to be a kingpin, she stopped praying for the sun to shine through her drab days, and resigned herself to embrace the rain.

Guess that's how she hooked up with Chico. Kenisha had been dazzled by his pretty olive skin, wavy hair, and bulky arms. Dazzled by his corporate job, and technical school education. Of course, all that dazzling occurred before her responsible boyfriend started hanging around her crack head brother, Kevin. By the time she gave birth to her third child, Chico had quit his good-paying job so he could give crack his undivided attention.

Now, the only time Brianna saw her crack head father, was when he made his first of the month visit. Begging for a loan that he knew his broke behind couldn't pay back. She remembered the first time she refused to give Chico her rent money. He punched her in the face so hard her teeth clickety-clacked. Grabbing the iron skillet that she'd been frying chicken in, she chased him out of her house. When she walked back in, and saw Jamal, her oldest child, standing in the kitchen holding a butcher knife, as his eyes blazed with fury, she swore right then that she would have nothing more to do with Chico and his crack demon.

100

Shaking her head to ward away bad memories, Kenisha grabbed a washcloth and towel from the hall closet. Jumping in the shower, she allowed the hot water to assault her weary bones. As the steam filled the small bathroom, she wallowed in the horror story her life had become. What next? How much can happen to a person before the Almighty decides it's time to pick on someone else?

"Ah, dawg." She knew she'd forgotten something. Bumping her head against the tiled wall of the shower, she turned the water off and stepped out. She had an appointment that might make her late picking Jamal up from school. Not wanting to leave it to chance, she decided to call Aisha to see if she could pick her son up.

Before she could get her clothes on and make it to the telephone, Chico knocked on her back door. She was familiar with his knock. It was the first of the month, baby, can I please get a loan kind of banging that rolled through her head twelve times a year.

"Don't I have enough to deal with?" She picked up the pink frilly robe James bought her on her fifteenth birthday. It had been soft and pretty, but the drudge of life had worn on it. Thought she would have replaced it long ago. But the kids kept coming, and the men kept leaving.

She picked up Jamal's leather belt, secured her tattered robe, stalked down stairs and flung open the back door. "What do you want, Chico?"

"Ah girl, quit tripping. You know you're happy to see me. Them hazel eyes of yours sparkle every time I come over here."

She ran her hands through her short layered hair as the skeleton strolled up to her, and puckered his lips. The five-day stench and sunken cheeks made Kenisha back up and give him the hand. "If it's money you want, my welfare check hasn't even arrived yet."

Bucked eyes, and a deep sigh accused Kenisha of misjudging him. "How you know I didn't come over here to see my beautiful little girl?"

"Did you happen to get a job and bring your beautiful little girl some child support? Cause, Brianna likes to eat."

"Why you got to be like that?" He leaned against the kitchen sink. "See, that's why I don't come by more often. You always trippin'."

Kenisha opened the back door. "Boy, who do you think you're fooling? You don't come by more 'cause the first only comes once a month." A strong wind blew her robe open, exposing two bony thighs.

"Girl you need to quit selling them food stamps. You know I like a woman with meat on her bones."

Kenisha rolled her eyes and waved him toward the coolness of the outdoor wind.

"Oh, so it's like that?" Pushing himself off the sink, he told her, "Just get Brianna down here. Let me see my baby girl and I'll be on my way."

"She ain't here. They spent the night over Aisha's."

Walking toward her, he got loud. "How many times have I told you not to have my daughter over your sorry sister's house?"

"When the telling comes with a check, that's when I'll start listening." Still holding the door open, she motioned him outdoors again.

He poked his index finger into the middle of her forehead. "Make sure my daughter is home the next time I come to see her."

He walked out. But before Kenisha slammed the door she told him, "Yeah, right. We'll see you in thirty days, Chico."

She sat on the couch as her body shook with rage. Her rage wasn't only directed at Chico. But at all the men who'd promised her sweetness, then made her swallow dung. She was tired. Wished she'd never met any of them. Sure wouldn't be in the fix she was in now if she'd waited until marriage to have sex. Maybe she should have signed up for karate classes when she was six or seven. That way she could have broken her mother's boyfriend's neck that night he took all her choices away.

Clicking on the TV, she hoped to find enjoyment in somebody else's drama. Dr. Phil was putting a smile on a woman's face whose house had been robbed and ransacked. "Ain't that 'bout nothing? My life is raggedy, but I don't see nobody offering me so much as a needle and thread to stitch it up." She turned off the TV and stood. Might as well just deal with it. She picked up the phone and dialed Aisha.

The phone rang three times before Aisha's angry voice protruded through the line. "What have I told you about calling my house so early?"

Caller ID wasn't meant for everybody. It was 10:45 in the morning. And Aisha's lazy behind was still in bed, screening calls. "You need to get up and fix breakfast. My kids have a hot meal every morning." Aisha yawned. "Your kids ain't no better than mine. They can walk downstairs and fix a bowl of cereal just like the rest of them monsters."

Rolling her eyes, Kenisha wondered why she'd agreed to let Diamond and Brianna spend the night over her sister's house. But she had been too tired to get on the number eight bus and pick them up. Blinking away unwanted tears, she allowed her fist to smash against her living room wall. Ever since her doctor told her about the cancer eating away at her body, her walls had gotten punched. When her doctor told her that having sex at an early age was one of the factors for cervical cancer, she'd wanted to kill the men that had paraded through her life; took what they wanted, then left her diseased. "I need you to pick Jamal up from school today."

"Oh, no. I've already got two of your kids over here. Dawg, Kenisha, I've got four kids of my own. What makes you think I want to baby sit another?"

Grabbing some tissue, and wiping the moisture from around her eyes, she said, "Look Aisha, I've got an appointment." Kenisha's third radiation treatment was scheduled for today. She'd missed her second appointment when Aisha promised to pick up her kids, but never showed. "It's important or I wouldn't ask."

Kenisha heard the rustling of the sheets as her sister sat up in bed.

"What's so special that you can't pick up your own son?"

"Nothing special. Just another rainy day."

CHAPTER 3

Deidre Clark Morris sat behind her oak desk trying to decide whether to respond to her emails. At last count, she had seventy unopened messages. She just couldn't make herself read another parent complaint about the athletic programs she was forced to cut. Didn't have the patience to deal with teachers complaining about old textbooks. The superintendent had already given her his 'sorry about your luck' look the last time she told him that she needed to replace the textbooks.

Today, she didn't have the energy to fight. Deidre had other things on her mind. Consuming things. Things between her, Johnson, and God. *Please God, don't let it come.*

It, was her monthly cycle. Due yesterday, but thankfully absent. If *it* didn't show up today, maybe she'd finally have some good news to report to Johnson.

Another email appeared in her inbox. This one was from Johnson. The header read, "How are you doing?" On an ordinary day, a simple message like that from her husband would have put a smile on her face. Would have made her think of the When A Man Loves A Woman song.

But today was not ordinary. This was the day she would either get her period or be pregnant. So she knew that her wonderful, loving husband's email really meant "After seven long years of wishing, and waiting, are you finally pregnant?"

Leave me alone. Those were the words she wanted to shout back across the email line. But salvation in the name of Jesus, and a couple deep breaths stopped her tirade. Consigning Johnson's email to the same devil the other seventy could go to, Deidre signed off her computer. It was three-thirty, the students had been gone since two-fifty. It was time she headed home herself.

A knock at her door stopped her from packing up. "Come in."

Mrs. Wilson, the stern-faced second grade teacher walked in with little Jamal Moore in tow. Deidre knew Jamal. Had greeted him several times in the hallway. He was always well groomed. One of the first things she noticed about Jamal, after his signature zigzag cornrows, was that his pants fit. Either he, or his mom didn't buy into that sloppy, hanging off your backside fad that most kids were wearing.

"What's up?" Deidre asked.

Pointing at Jamal, Mrs. Wilson told her, "His mother didn't pick him up. I need to leave him with you."

"I was just getting ready to leave, Mrs. Wilson. I can't stay with him today."

Mrs. Wilson gave Deidre a piercing glare. "Now I understand that you are the principal of this school, and therefore more important than the rest of us, but you are also the one that closed down the after care program---"

Deidre held up her hand. "The superintendent closed down our after care program, Mrs. Wilson. Not me."

With hands on healthy hips, Mrs. Wilson told her, "I don't care if it was you or the superintendent. You didn't stop him. And you promised to take turns watching these errant children. Well, it's your turn."

Deidre looked toward Jamal. With the exchange going on in front of him, he couldn't be feeling very wanted, or cared about. For goodness sake, his mother had left him to fend for himself. Abandoned him. He didn't need to listen to this babysitting tug-of-war. "Go home Mrs. Wilson, Jamal and I will be just fine."

Dismissing Mrs. Wilson as she harrumphed out of the office, Deidre smiled at Jamal. "What's your number? We'll get your mom on the phone. She'll be here in no time, you'll see."

She opened her desk drawer, grabbed the Reese's Cup she'd been saving for a special occasion, and tossed it to Jamal. She stood and picked up the telephone. Her smile disappeared. The oozing warmth between her legs screamed, "Failure." With as much composure as she could muster, she put down the phone. "I'll be right back."

Picking up her purse, she ran down the hall to the teacher's restroom. In the stall, sitting on the toilet, her worse nightmare was confirmed. "Oh God. Oh God, no." She did everything right. She'd used that chart religiously. She and Johnson had waited until her body temperature was at the right level. How could she not be pregnant? Banging her fist against the bathroom stall, she declared, "It's my turn, God." But, no matter how much she wanted it to be, it was not her turn. Would probably never be her turn.

She put her elbows on her thighs, hands over her face and cried as if she'd carried a baby to full term, watched him play in the backyard, grow into a young man, then held him, as he slowly died in her arms.

Twenty minutes later, Jamal found her that way. He tapped on the stall door. "Mrs. Morris, what's wrong?"

"I-I g-got my period," she blurted between gasps. She clamped her hand over her mouth as her eyes widened. The superintendent had been itching to fire her, he'd certainly do it now. How could she blurt such a thing out to a seven-year-old child?

Jamal smirked. "My Mama always screams, 'Thank You, Jesus' when she gets her period. The only time I heard her cry was when Mr. Friendly – that's what Mama calls it – came late one month."

Although she hated to admit it, Jamal's statement caused her to be upset with God. Women who didn't want children seemed to spit them out, while she and Johnson remained childless.

She closed her eyes, blinking away the remnants of tears as she thought of her husband. The day they met, he'd overwhelmed her with his deep dimpled smile. Scared her, when he declared that he believed in destiny, and she would be his wife. But the following week she was hooked, so into him, that when he told her how many children he wanted, she couldn't bring herself to tell him that two doctors had pronounced her infertile.

She should have told him. But he was all she'd ever wanted. Their love was so new she'd been terrified of losing him. After the Lord saved her soul, she'd thought, that if she charted her fertile periods and prayed....

"Mrs. Morris?"

Sniffling, Deidre wiped the tears from her face. "I-I'm sorry Jamal. I'll be out in a second." She blew her nose, took the pad out of her purse and lined her underwear with it. Flushing the toilet, she adjusted her clothes before opening the stall.

As if he were talking a lunatic down from a ledge, he asked, "Do you need me to get you anything?"

Washing and drying her hands, Deidre shook her head.

"When I'm sad, Mama holds my hand. That always makes me feel better." He stretched his hand. "Do you want to try it?"

Deidre's heart swelled with love for this boy who reached out to her when she needed it most. She grabbed his hand as they walked back to her office.

He squeezed her hand. "Feel better?"

A tear trickled down her cheek. "Much. Thank you, Jamal."

Back in her office, Deidre put her files in her briefcase. "If you don't mind, Jamal, I'd like to go home. I'll call your mom and give her my telephone number and address."

"That's fine with me. Just as long as you let her know where I'll be. I wouldn't want her to worry."

Deidre almost told him that she was sure his mother wasn't all that concerned. If she were, she wouldn't have forgotten to pick him up. That was the other beef she had with God. She and Johnson would be great parents. They'd never leave their children to fend for themselves. But alas, the babies were gifted to the unfit, while she, Deidre Clark-Morris, babysat.

CHAPTER 4

Memories, like demons, kicked Kenisha around. Weak and beaten as she lay on her hospital bed after radiation, the ghosts of yesterday reclaimed her soul.

"Dynasty, girl you ain't right."

"Ah, stop your crying," she told Kenisha as she raked the cards off the table. "We won fair and square and you know it."

Kenisha sat back and huffed. "Just deal the cards." They were playing Spades. Terrell, Kenisha's boyfriend was her partner. And Clyde was Dynasty's partner. Although the stiff way Dynasty was treating Clyde made Kenisha wonder if he was still her life partner. She turned to Clyde. "You need to stop letting your bad habits rub off on my sister. She was a nice girl before she started messing around with you."

Laughter escaped the mouth of three of the card players. But Kenisha noticed something akin to regret dancing around her sister's eyes. Dynasty's silence changed the mood, caused the game to end sooner than it normally would have.

Terrell stood and stretched his long, athletic body. "Guess it's time to go. I got people to see."

Kenisha frowned. "Thought you said you were going to let that mess alone?"

He walked around the table, bent down and kissed her forehead. "Girl, you're man has gotta handle his business. How would it look if I let them thugs get away with creeping on my turf?"

Kenisha awkwardly pushed her big-bellied body out of her chair and stood. "It would look like you had finally gotten your senses together. Like you were ready to grow up and be a father to our child."

Palming her belly, Terrell told her, "Girl, I'm gon' always take care of mine. Believe that."

Gently rubbing the side of his face she tried again. "I just don't want you to get hurt, Terrell. Every thug on them streets is not gon' back down just cause you mean and mad."

He moved her hand from his face. "Just have my steak ready when I get back here. Come on Clyde, let's go handle our business."

"I'll be out there in a minute," Clyde said. Terrell walked out and got in the truck. Clyde turned to Dynasty. "Can I talk to you for a minute?"

Eyes downcast, Dynasty told him, "Nothing left to say."

"Don't be like this, Dy."

"It's over Clyde. Just let me go, okay?"

He picked up a chair and threw it across Kenisha's living room. Dynasty jumped up and ran behind the couch.

Kenisha yelled outside. "Terrell, come get your boy!"

"You're not just gon' dismiss me like this, Dy. I've done too much for you."

With the couch between them, and Terrell on his way back in the house Dynasty let loose. "Yeah, you've done a lot for me. But you've done a lot more to me. Don't you get it Clyde? You ruined everything we had when you made me miscarry our baby."

"Why you gotta start with her? We've got things to do," Terrell called from the door.

"This ain't over, Dy," he told her as he walked out the door.

Dynasty came from behind the couch and yelled at Clyde as he jumped in Terrell's truck. "Oh, it's over alright. So stop coming over to my sister's house. I don't want to play cards with you. I don't want to talk to you. Don't want to know you exist. Do you hear me, Clyde?" She slammed the door, locked it, then sat down and cried.

Kenisha went to her sister and softly rubbed her back. "It'll be okay, Dy."

She looked up. "When? I haven't seen an okay day since your crazy mama birthed me."

"She was your crazy mama first."

They both laughed, then Dynasty asked, "You got any Kool-Aid?"

Kenisha went to the kitchen, poured two glasses of orange Kool-Aid, walked back into the living room and handed her sister a glass. "I had no idea, Dy. You told us that you lost the baby because of some kind of accident."

Dynasty took a couple gulps, then sat the glass down. "Yeah, Clyde *accidentally* kicked it out of me."

Kenisha flopped down on the couch next to her sister. "I didn't know, Dy. Dawg. What made him do it?"

Sniffling, and wiping the tears from her face Dynasty asked, "Besides being crazy?"

Trying not to laugh, Kenisha nudged her sister. "What happened?"

"We were at MJ's drinking and having a good time when Carl walked in."

"You're ex-boyfriend, Carl?"

"Exactly. Well Carl spoke to me, and I stupidly spoke back. Clyde snatched me out of that club, took me home and preceded to beat me from one room to the next. He said that my baby probably belonged to Carl. That's when he kicked me. Over and over again."

Kenisha rubbed Dynasty's back. "If I'd known, Dynasty, there's no way I would have let Terrell bring that dog in here."

"Don't worry about it. The sad part is, I think I still love him."

"How you gon' love somebody that did some mess like that to you?"

"I never said I wanted to love him, Kenisha. I'm all messed up, tore up inside. I just can't stop my heart from loving his no good behind."

They sat there in silence for a while. Both recognizing the irrational desires of the heart. The longings that just couldn't be denied, even when danger signs glared in their face. "Well, if you really love him, have you thought about giving him a second chance?"

Why, why, why, did she think Clyde could change? Not a day went by that Kenisha didn't long to talk to her sister, her best friend again. But her sister was dead, and she had sent her back into the arms of the man who murdered her – this was her greatest sin. Cancer was her atonement. Sitting up, she locked her memories back in the past and put on her clothes so she could leave the hospital and go home to her children.

Before leaving the hospital, she found a pay phone and called Aisha. "Hey, I'm on my way home. Can you bring the kids to me?"

"Well, it took you long enough. My God Kenisha, it's almost six o'clock."

"I know, I know. It couldn't be helped. Did Jamal have any homework?"

"How would I know. I thought Jamal was with you."

Screaming into the phone Kenisha asked, "Are you telling me, you didn't pick my son up? I called you this morning and asked you to get him for me."

Snapping her fingers. "My bad, Kenisha. I forgot."

Still screaming, Kenisha told her, "You better borrow John's car and bring yourself to Good Samaritan Hospital and pick me up so I can find my son."

"What are you doing at the hospital?"

"Don't waist time asking me stupid questions. Get you butt over here now."

"Alright, Kenisha, calm down. I'll be there in a few minutes. Geeze, I'm sorry."

"Well that just makes it all better, doesn't it?" Kenisha asked then slammed the phone down without waiting for a reply.

CHAPTER 5

Oreo Ice Cream and pepperoni and ham pizza was a combination for pregnant women. But Deidre sat defiantly on her family room sectional, with no baby in her stomach, wolfing down ice cream and pizza anyway. She pointed at a video on the coffee table. "Put that in the VCR," she told Jamal.

Jamal read the movie title as he picked it up. "You like this old stuff?"

"Old stuff? You mean classic, right?"

He popped the movie in the VCR and punched play. "Call it whatever you like. All I'm saying is if it's a black and white flick, it's old."

In between a mouth full of ice cream and pizza, Deidre laughed. The sound was almost foreign to her. Laughter had been missing in her life since guilt over not being able to produce Johnson's child took hold of her, and her good job became an evil nightmare. Since she could do nothing about the child issue, Deidre tried desperately to push Johnson out of her mind. She knew she should have emailed him back at work, or telephoned him so he would know that she wasn't pregnant. But it was too hard to let the words slip out of her mouth. Too hard to hear Johnson's not-again sigh. So, as she sat back and pretended to watch "It's a Wonderful Life" with Jamal. Deidre thought on the problems at work.

Frank Thomas was the Superintendent over the city of Dayton schools. He'd given Deidre a hard time every since he took the position five years ago. His lack of trust in her ability to run her school effectively was taking its toll on her performance. Which was another blow to Deidre's self esteem and her faith in God. As a Christian, performing well was important to Deidre. She felt that she not only work for Frank Thomas, but for God. And when he belittled her efforts, she pictured God looking down on her shaking his finger.

Deidre put her bucket of ice cream on the coffee table as a thought ran through her mind. Maybe she couldn't get pregnant because of all the stress on her job.

"Do you think this getting your wings stuff is for real?"

Remembering that she had company, Deidre turned to Jamal. "What?"

"The angel in this movie. Do you think that's true?"

"Do I think what's true?"

Jamal rolled his eyes, and pointed at the TV. Clarence the angel was telling a bartender that he needed to help someone in order to get his wings. "Do you think that's true?"

She turned her face toward the TV. "Oh. I'm not sure."

"What about angels? Do you think they're real?"

Sometimes I wonder. "Yes, of course angels are real."

"Turn left here." When Aisha missed the turn, Kenisha jumped up and down in the front seat of the car. "Where are you going? I told you to turn left back there."

"I was going too fast to turn. Calm down, Kenisha I'm turning around."

"I'll calm down when I get to my son. How could you forget about him, Aisha? You ain't right."

Making a U-turn in the street, Aisha said, "I already told you I was sorry about that. He's over at his principal's house right? So he's safe."

Kenisha rolled her eyes as she sat back in her seat, and glared at her sister. She just didn't get it. It's a wonder that Children's Services didn't visit her more than once a year. *The annual check-up,* Aisha jokingly referred to the visits she received from social workers.

Kenisha would be mortified if some social worker came to her house accusing her of being an unfit mother. She was so frantic about Jamal being left at school. While waiting on her sister to pick her up, Kenisha called the school, but only got the voicemail. She called her mother to see if Jamal had called her, but her mother was drunk and couldn't remember. Then Kenisha tried her home voicemail, hoping that Jamal had left her a message. That's when relief swept over her as she wrote down the address Jamal's principal left for her.

"Why were you at the hospital anyway?"

"Turn right here, she lives on this street."

"Don't ignore me," Aisha said as she turned the corner. "Why were you at the hospital?"

"Slow down, look for 6280. And it's none of your business."

"Oh, so I can play taxi, but I don't get to know nothing."

Kenisha pointed at red bricked house. "Pull over, Aisha. This is it."

Aisha leaned her head against the windowsill. "Wow. Jamal sure knows who to go home with. Leave it to him to pick some rich white lady."

"Jamal's principal isn't white. She's a sista." She got out of the car and walked across hunter green grass, smelled the fragrance of fresh pine mulch that surrounded the trees. Knocking on the door, Kenisha put a smile on her face, and tried to forget that all she wanted to do was to find a bed, and lay down.

"So what did you think of the movie?" Deidre asked Jamal as Clarence got his wings.

He got up and took the tape out of the VCR. As he returned to his seat he told her, "My mom acted like that guy for a while."

"Which guy?"

"The one who thought everybody would have been better off if he'd never been born."

Cautiously, Deidre asked. "Why does your mom think that?"

"She doesn't now. But after my aunt died, I would hear her crying and saying stuff about it all being her fault." He looked

116

down at his hands. Realized he was still holding the tape, sat it on the coffee table. "I watch these old movies a lot with my mom." He pointed at the slices of pizza on the table. "My mom likes pepperoni and ham pizza too.

Deidre recognized the change in subjects and let it happen.

"You know what?" Jamal asked her. "You remind me of my mother."

"Like how?"

"Well, you're nice, and you like kids."

Deidre smiled at Jamal. "How do you know I like kids?"

"Ah, come on Mrs. Morris. All the kids at school know that you are fair. You don't just ignore us because we're kids. You listen."

Hearing that from Jamal made Deidre feel much better about the strides she made at Miami Chapel. Lately, with how her boss had been treating her she started feeling like a failure. Like, maybe somebody else could take over as principle and do a much better job. "Thanks, Jamal. I appreciate your saying that."

"It's true. All the kids talk about how cool you are." Jamal eyes turned sad as he shook his head. "It's too bad you weren't pregnant today. You'd make a great mom."

The smile left Deidre lips as sadness invaded her eyes. She stood and began clearing the pizza, ice cream container, and cups off the coffee table. *Lord, please make the pain go away.* But the pain would not move. Tears trickled down her face as she walked into the kitchen.

Jamal followed her and sat on the stool behind the counter. "I'm sorry. I didn't mean to make you sad again."

She grabbed a napkin off the counter and wiped the tears from her face, then blew her nose. "I'm all right, don't worry abou---"

The door bell rang.

Jamal jumped up. "That's my mom."

Throwing the napkin in the waste basket Deidre told Jamal, "Well, let's go let her in."

***

Kenisha had few dreams. But the one that stuck with her was about moving her children into a nice home in a nice neighborhood where they could go outside and play without ducking gunfire. Every Sunday when Mr. Haddley, her elderly next door neighbor was finished reading his newspaper, he would knock on her door and give her the Home section. Kenisha poured over the pages. Taking in the square footage, and the acreage of the homes. Once, she even took the bus to a home aroma event. She walked through three and four hundred dollar homes. Asking questions about the structure and feeling the etching in the columns as if she could be an interested buyer. She knew what a quality home looked like. That's why her mouth hung open and she couldn't even say hello when Mrs. Morris opened the door and she stepped into the foyer.

"It's nice isn't it mama. Like those houses you look at on Sunday."

"You ain't lied about that, Jamal." She stepped past Deidre looking at the spacious open floor plan. The winding staircase. "This house is off the chain."

"Mmmph," Deidre cleared her throat.

Kenisha turned toward Deidre. "Oh, hey. Gurl, I was 'bout to take a tour of this mug. Thought I was in one of them Show homes for a minute. How you doing?"

"I'm fine," Deidre told her, then added, "Thanks for picking Jamal up."

Kenisha caught the college girl attitude Miss Thang was throwing at her. She was about to go there with her, but after the day she'd had, she just didn't have the energy. So she simply told her, "You don't have to thank me. That's my job."

Deidre turned to Jamal. "Go get your things." She turned back to Kenisha once Jamal was out of sight. "It looks like you forgot your job today."

"Look, lady. I don't know what your problem is, but my son has never been left at your school before. I pick him up on time everyday."

"Not today."

"Once, okay. One time out of a year."

"Once is too many."

Kenisha gave Deidre the hand. "Whatever."

"How can you be so nonchalant," Deidre kept her voice to a whisper as she told Kenisha off. "Jamal is your son. He should be precious, and far more important than any errand you had to run."

Kenisha continued to roll her eyes with the five finger disconnect still in Deidre's face.

"If you think I'm going to let you ruin Jamal's life you can think again. I'm calling Children Services first thing in the morning. We'll see how smug you are then."

Kenisha's hand came down. "Look lady, you've got it all wrong."

Tears flowed from Deidre's eyes as she pointed into the family room where Jamal was gathering his stuff. "I'm not going to let you hurt him. A mother should love and care for her child. Not put him in harms way."

"That's my heart. Jamal knows he's my heart. I'd never do anything to hurt him."

Deidre wiped at the tears. "Tell it to Children Services."

"W-w-wait." No social worker was going to call her unfit. Before Kenisha could stop herself she blurted out, "I have cancer, okay. I was at the hospital getting a radiation treatment."

"What a terrible thing to say."

"It's more like, a terrible thing to have. But it's true. You can call my doctor if you want." She dug in her purse and produced a small white business card. "Here. Call him if you don't believe me."

Jamal walked back in the room looking from his mom to Mrs. Morris. His mom had this angry look on her face and Mrs. Morris was standing there with her mouth hanging open. "Is something wrong?"

"No baby. Let's just go. I need to get out of here," Kenisha told him as she grabbed his hand and swung open the front door.

"Wait," Deidre screamed.

Kenisha turned around to face her accuser again. "What else you got to say, lady?"

"Can I pray with you?"

Kenisha scoffed. "What do you want to do; pray that God makes me a better mother or something?"

"No, I believe you that this was a one time incident. I want to pray about your situation."

Kenisha let go of Jamal's hand and told him, "Go get in the car with you aunt and your sisters." When Jamal was gone Kenisha turned back to Deidre and confided, "I don't think God is interested in helping me."

"All you need is a little bit of faith, Kenisha. Trust me, God will meet you right where you are." Deidre couldn't believe that she was saying this stuff. Hadn't she determined that God wasn't interested in helping her just a few hours ago herself?

"I don't know. Let me think about it," Kenisha said as she walked out of Deidre's house.

"You've got my number. Call me anytime – day or night if you want to talk or pray."

CHAPTER 7

Kenisha made hamburger helper as soon as she got home. Fed her kids and then put Diamond and Brianna to bed. Jamal was like her, a night owl. She let him stay up with her, but never past eleven. His company usually helped her not to feel so lonely. But tonight, when he looked at her with those sad brown eyes, she wished she'd put him to bed with the girls.

"You got cancer?"

Kenisha got up, went into the kitchen and started running some dish water.

Jamal followed her. "Do you have cancer?"

She turned to face him. "What you know about cancer?"

A tear trickled down his young face. "I know that my friend Joey's grandmother just died from it."

Kenisha turned off the dish water and sat down at the small kitchen table. She patted the seat next to her, and her son joined her. "Now, Jamal, you know that Joey's grandmother was old, right?"

"Right."

"But I'm not old. I'm too young to die." She put his small hand in hers and rubbed from his hand to his elbow, up and down. "So don't think like that okay."

"You've got it, don't you? I heard you tell Mrs. Morris that you had cancer."

Jamal was wise beyond his years, always had been. Kenisha had never been able to hide anything from him. No since trying now. She lowered her head, twisted her lips. "Yeah, baby. I've got cancer."

He cried. Kenisha held her son, as his tears flowed. His body jerked back and forth, but he held on to his mother tightly. "Come on, Jamal. Stop all this crying. I'm going to need you to be strong for me. You've always been my little helper. And I'm going to need you now."

Slowly, he released his hold, sat back in his chair and dried his eyes.

It was all Kenisha could do not to throw her own pity party. But she had to be strong for Jamal. "Are you going to help me through this, Jamal?"

"I can do it. I'll take care of you, Mama."

She grabbed him, and hugged him tight. "That's my little man." It was hard, but she pulled away from the embrace, patted his hand. "Everything's going to be okay. You'll see."

Jamal gave her a weak smile.

"Off to bed with you. I'm going to finish these dishes and go to bed myself. We can watch a movie tomorrow night. Okay?"

Jamal got up without arguing about going to bed before eleven. "But, Mom, you need to take care of yourself too. Did you pray with Mrs. Morris tonight like she asked?

No, but I told her I would think about it."

Jamal kissed his mother on the cheek and walked away.

The tears she held while talking to Jamal fell as she watched him walk away. How could this be happening to her? What was God thinking, giving her cancer? Didn't he know she had three children to raise?

Getting up, she walked back to the sink and started putting the glasses in the water. Once again, she had found herself in another situation that proved God didn't care about her or her children. She swished a drinking glass around in the water a few times. Pulled it out of the water, but instead of rinses the bubbles from the glass she threw it against the kitchen door. "You're not fair," she screamed at God as the shattered glass cascaded down the wall.

All you need is a little bit of faith.

Kenisha turned around in her kitchen trying to determine who had just spoke to her. No one was there. "Who said that?" she whispered. It was the words that Jamal's principal had spoken to her earlier that evening, but this time when she heard it, the words weren't coming from Deidre. And the more Kenisha thought about it – the voice she heard wasn't within her house either; it came from the depth of her heart. Like God was speaking to her personally.

She walked out of the kitchen headed toward the living room. All the while she was wondering, *after all she had been through is God actually telling me that just a little bit of faith can turn my situation around?*

She picked up the telephone in the living room and dialed Jamal's principal. The phone rang three times Deidre answered it. Kenisha told her, "I'm ready to pray now."

"Kenisha? Is that you?"

"Yeah, it's me."

"I was just praying for you," Deidre told her. "I think God had us cross paths on purpose today. I had been feeling really down about not being able to have children and then there you were, and I began to believe that God could do the impossible again."

"That's kind of funny," Kenisha told her. "You feeling down about not having kids and I feel bad about having too many kids."

"I guess life is just weird that way," Deidre confessed.

"But you know what I learned today?" Kenisha asked Deidre

"No, what did you learn?"

"All you need is just a little bit of faith, Deidre. Just believe that God can change your situation."

"Okay, I'll do that. Now let's pray."

Contact **Vanessa Miller** at: www.vanessamiller.com email: vmiller-01@earthlink.net

Surrender, And The Music Will Come
By: Deryl Ann Roundtree

As a child, I was nicknamed 'Grouchy' because I was always mad at someone for some reason or another. I was the oldest girl and from about the age of five I had, in my opinion, been given too much responsibility. I had to help take care of my younger siblings, learn to cook, and also iron my mom's white nurse uniforms and my father's white shirts. And this was back in the day when you had to use that gunky blue starch mix that made me sick to my stomach.

One day as I sat, angry with my lips poked out; my father stated that I was always mad because I never got what I wanted. 'Well, isn't that a good reason?' I thought. Mind you, I 'thought' those words and would never say such a thing out loud and risk having to pick myself up from the floor.

Later my stubborn attitude turned into my 'Independent Single Woman' phase. I drove a pickup truck so I wouldn't have to beg another trifling man to help me move this or that. I paid my own bills and did my own thing. I did whatever I wanted, whenever I wanted and however I wanted to do it!

That stubbornness even prompted me to suddenly pick up and move miles away from my family to a hot new city and a new life; far away from all of my stupid mistakes and bad choices that were piling up on my shoulders. In my new town, I used to go to the nightclubs, not really to drink or to meet guys, but to dance! I loved to free my spirit by dancing to the loud music that seemed to take away all of my cares, at least for a couple hours anyway. I just had to dance. *I must dance!* No way was anyone evah-evah going to tell me what to do, when to do it, or how to do it. I was not surrendering my will to anyone!

Especially not to an unfamiliar but clear voice in my head that warned me not to get involved with the 6'3" gorgeous man that stopped me in the grocery store about a year after I had moved to this new town. I'll call him 'that boy'. As I marveled at his unbelievably white teeth, that unfamiliar voice actually told me that he was lying through those teeth. But since I did not know who that voice in my head was, I kept right on listening as this hunk of a man began to spin his web.

The next five years is a blur of extreme mental, emotional, spiritual and sexual abuse that I suffered from 'that boy'. I was even thrown in jail, spent time in a mental ward and was also rendered homeless for a short period of time as a result of our relationship. After I finally got up the nerve to end our relationship it took five more years for my mind, my heart and my spirit to heal from all the damage that had been done.

But God!!! Did you know that the word 'But' cancels out whatever precedes it? My pastor often tells us that God will not waste anything that we have been through in our lives. I'll never forget the day I was crying out to the Lord about all of the horrible things I had suffered in my life; when that now familiar voice asked me, "How can you possibly help those others out there who are suffering, if you had not had a taste of what they are going through?" It was indeed a light bulb moment for God's purpose for my life. Ezekiel 2:8 reads, 'But look, I have made you as obstinate (stubborn) and hard-hearted as they are. Wow, Lord! Do you mean to tell me that it was *You* who made me so pig-headed? Did you notice how God started that scripture with the word 'But'? That tells me that He has x'd out all of the mess that I have gone through in my life and He is now using the stubbornness that He gave me, for *His purposes* and not for doing my own thing. Hello!

So now I am Single and Saved and I have learned to embrace my God-given stubbornness and to boldly do what the Lord tells me to do; whatever, whenever and however He tells me to do it! And that includes even forgiving 'that boy'. Oh it was not easy and it did not happen overnight. But when I look back on all the things I did in my past and all of the people I hurt with my stubborn pride and razor sharp tongue; how can I not forgive 'that boy', when the Lord has forgiven me all of my sins. You see, forgiveness is like a blooming onion. You have to peel away the hurt, crusted layer by crusted layer until you find that underneath all of that pain, your heart is still as warm and loving as it was before.

But folks, forgiveness won't happen until you want to free yourself and be healed *more* than you want to punish the one who hurt you. Besides, if you don't forgive, Matthew 6:15 tells us that the Lord will not forgive us; and that is motivation enough for me to get down from my high horse and release the memories of pain suffered long ago.

You know just the other day, as I was praying and asking God to bring back the joy and laughter and dance that I had prior to that abusive relationship; I heard that ole familiar voice of the Holy Spirit tells me, "Surrender and the music will come." I then made the decision that no matter how stubborn I may feel, I will surrender my all and all to God; because you see, *I must dance!*

Deryl A. Roundtree has been writing since she was a child. She has written skits, plays and monologues. "Surrender And The Music Will Come" is her first entry in an anthology. It is Deryl's hope to one day write a novel.

Contact Deryl at: email: derylrountree@yahoo.com

Bee in My Bonnet – RDW III
By: Linda Wattley

I write this story with Mary, the mother of Jesus in mind. She had no ideal what her future held. Who could have told her she would give birth to the Savior of the world? She became a mother of a son destined to teach her the true meaning of love. My first born son also taught me about steadfast love and the necessity to know God.

In 1978, I married Robert D. Wattley Jr. We lived in Fort Wayne, Indiana. About six months later I realized I was not ready to be a mom. I made an appointment to get birth control pills.

"I have an appointment to see Dr. Harris."

"Sign in and fill out these forms. We need your insurance card and driver's license." The nurse said as she handed me the registration packet.

I filled out the forms, and waited to see the doctor. When the doctor came into the room, he told me I was pregnant and asked what did I want to do?

"I came to get birth control pills. What do you mean, what do I want to do?"

"You're pregnant. Are you keeping your baby?"

Grabbing my white paper gown, I began to feel dizzy as I plopped down on the chair and attempted to grasp what he'd just told me. My mouth became dry and I was at a loss for words. Part of me was angry with the doctor because he would not look at me when he spoke nor did he understand that I did not believe what he was saying.

"Are you in the right room?" I asked him. "There must be some mistake."

He walked over to me and looked me in the eyes. "I'm sorry I was so impersonal with you ma'am. You're pregnant and it looks like your due date based on your last cycle is October 12th. Do you have any questions?"

"Are you sure?"

Laughing and revealing a pleasant smile, he answered. "Yes, I am sure. We can do another test if you'd like."

Both of us were more comfortable now and able to begin our patient and doctor relationship on a pleasant basis. He picked up his clip board and left the room. I slowly got dressed and began to entertain the idea of being pregnant with my first child.

"Congratulations, Mrs. Wattley," the nurse said to me as I walked out the office.

While driving home, I kept going over in my mind how I was going to tell my husband about my news. Usually I am the first one home but tonight, Bob was home relaxing in front of the television.

"Hi baby, are you going to church tonight?" Bob asked as he picked up his ice-filled glass of Sprite off the table.

"Yeah, I have something to tell you," I said with a complex yet happy look on my face.

"No, I have something to tell you first. You are pregnant. You are going to have a boy. He is going to be born on my birthday and he is going to have my name."

"Get out of here! How did you know?"

"I just know. Yeah, baby he is going to have my name."

"You don't know everything. He's not due until the twelfth of October!"

"Don't matter. Watch what I tell you. He will be born on September the 25th, on my birthday."

That night I went to church and Elder Clark anointed my head with oil and prayed for the seed in my womb. I was slain in the spirit. In our church, Wings of Deliverance, the Holy Ghost was known to visit often. The first thing I did when I stood up was to hold my stomach with both my hands.

"Don't worry, darling. God has poured His spirit into your womb. Hallelujah!" Elder Clark said as he began to praise God; the rest of the church joined with him in praising with song. The organist and drummer were on fire that night. It was as though we were led into celebration.

It was not difficult guessing what I was having. The old saying: when you carry it low it is a boy was written all over me especially coming down to my last month. All was going well. But on September 25th, I kept running back and forth to the bathroom. The phone rang. I thought it was my husband. It turned out to be my sister-in-law, Marcille.

"How are you doing?"

"I'm fine. I just keep going to the bathroom peeing."

"Girl, are you sure that is what you are doing? Sounds like your water broke."

"I don't think so. My bed isn't wet."

"I'm taking you to the hospital. It's time."

By the time she hung up the phone, I felt my first contraction. I had gone into labor. We left a message at my husband's job and went to the hospital. The contractions began to come closer together. By the time the doctor put on his rubber gloves, a bouncing baby boy came forth.

I remember looking at my son as the doctor held him up. He was so perfect and beautiful to me. I started speaking in tongues. Yeah, even while shivering, exhausted and aching from the waist down I had to praise God for giving me this wonderful and precious gift. Tears immediately seeped from my eyes as I held him in my arms. I wanted to share this moment with his father.

"You did it. I have a boy!" My husband said as they rolled me down the hall to my room."

"Bobby, he already looks like you."

"I have the best birthday present!"

129

"You sure do." I said with a smile not having a problem being wrong.

"What's his name?"

"I'm not sure yet."

"His name is Robert Dennis Wattley, III." He yelled.

"Amen!" I said as I dosed off into a deep sleep.

He was the first grandson born on both sides of our families plus he was the third Robert added to the Wattley family. His Grandmother Wattley found it a joy calling him the king and our little prince.

I remember one day looking into my son's eyes. He was such a happy baby. I nicknamed him Binkie. I would take him to church with me every time I went. At eighteen months he was fascinated with a preacher that held on to his microphone as he preached and walked the isles. I knew he would get excited watching but I didn't think much about it until one day we were visiting my beautician in her home to get my hair done.

After a few twirls of the curling iron, Martha sat down to catch her breath. Binkie awakened from his nap and picked up a toy that fit into his hand like a microphone. He started babbling. We heard him mention Jesus and the Holy Ghost but we couldn't make out the other words. He began to slowly raise one leg after the other and walk towards us just as the preacher he loves to watch had done. His whole demeanor was that of the preacher. We looked at each other in awe. This child was not even two years old and he was preaching under the anointing of the Holy Spirit. He walked over to Martha and put his left hand upon her head. She immediately lifted both hands unto God and started weeping. I felt the anointing upon my son and began to thank God. He turned and walked back to his pillow on the floor and lay down.

"Girl, I had a headache. It's gone! I had that headache for three days. God used that baby to heal me" Martha said.

I was speechless. I could not get this little body out of my mind; how it took on a glow, and the ministerial demeanor of a real preacher.

God blessed us with another son, Marcus. He too was a precious jewel. Binkie was so filled with strength and energy I knew I had to have another child to play with him. He was a daredevil and challenged his body all the time. His body looked like a compact football player's body.

One morning I had given him a bath and was letting the water out of the bath tub. Binkie at the age of three walked out of the bathroom and went into our bedroom where the bedroom window was up. I came out of the bathroom and stood in the hall way shocked. Binkie was perched like a bird on the window seal. Now bear in mind, there was no ledge. He was relaxing on the window frame both elbows resting on his knees; naked as a jay bird enjoying the morning sky. Any move at all and he would have dropped three stories down.

My husband had returned to put the screen in the window. He looked at me like I was crazy because I was just standing there immobile and unable to speak.

"What's the matter?" He asked.

I could not talk. I just pointed to the window. He saw our son perched on the window frame. He gave me the shhhhhhh sign with his hand. Like a cat, he entered the bedroom in one motion he took his arm and then pulled him into the room. My husband had nothing to say until Binkie was safe, neither did I as the tears fell from my eyes.

"Boy, you could have fallen and we would have had to take care of you for the rest of your life!" My husband shouted feeling free to show signs of fear.

Bobby handed Binkie to me and then embraced us both.

"Bobby, I don't know what I would have done if you weren't here."

"Don't think about it. I am here."

Binkie looked at us as though we had lost our minds. He could not understand why we were so upset because he sensed no danger.

I know there is a God. Robert D. Wattley III kept his parents in need of the Lord at all times. My husband, bless his heart was a free spirited person, and trusted that things would always be alright. This particular day, he trusted his friend's sister to take care of our sons while he played basketball. I was gone to class. But when class was over, I drove down the street to our home and found all my husbands' buddies looking in bushes and knocking on doors. My husband looked like he had seen a ghost. He did not say anything to me. I walked into the house to see my boys. Marcus was asleep and Binkie was no where to be found.

"Bobby, where is Binkie?"

"Cortez's sister was watching him."

"Where are they? I want to see my baby."

"She, she....went to the bathroom...."

"What's the matter? What's going on?" I asked feeling mighty scared by now.

"I, I ....don't know...."

"Oh, God! Where is my baby?"

"Help me, Lord! Tell me where my son is, please!" I cried.

I did not see my husband anymore. I was pulling the hair on my head by now looking up to the sky, waiting for God to tell me where my son was. Then, I heard it as plain as day.

Go to Lynell's house. Get in your car and drive to Lynell's house.

I jumped in my car. Tears rolling down my face and I drove over two miles to my friends' house. As soon as my car pulled up in front of her house, I saw Binkie standing in his big picture-sized glass window crying for his mother. Hallelujah!

Once we were visiting my father who lived on a hill. We just walked in the door and turned around to speak to everybody. We look around, no Binkie then we hear car horns blowing like crazy. He had run out the back door to the front of the house and was across the street heading for the playground in a matter of seconds. The cars blew their horns but not one car came close to hitting him. He looked at us again wondering why we were so upset.

I had my son seated in the back seat of a large four door Oldsmobile. It just so happened I looked in my rearview mirror and he was not there. That little fella had opened the car door and rolled out in the middle of the street. I stopped my car right where I was, and ran behind it to find Binkie sitting in the middle of the street without a scratch on him.

Binkie Becomes Bobby

Two and a half years later, as fate would have it, a week before my husband's and Binkies' birthday, my husband was killed in a car accident. In that moment, Binkie became Bobby in the hearts and minds of those who saw my husband's spirit in his eyes and demeanor. At the age of five, he became the little man of the house.

Bobby was treasured by my mother-in-law. His grandmother gave him everything his little heart desired and then some. Her philosophy: *The Secret is in Giving* was what she lived by. She gave to any and everybody. She like the preacher with the microphone captivated Bobby creating a conscious of wealth to his growing mind. She called him Binkie-man and he was the leader of her four grandchildren. Let grandmother tell it, he and all her grandchildren were royalty and should never settle for less in life.

In elementary school, there was a day once a week called "Show and Tell". The average child would have to share the same toy over and over, not Bobby. Every week there was a brand new toy. One day, I picked him up from school. The teacher was waiting for me.

"Mrs. Wattley, do you have a minute?"

"Sure."

"Bobby has started his own business here." She said as she laughed.

I signaled for him to come join our discussion. He came over blushing as he looked away knowing what the teacher was talking about.

"He sells candy bars; bye two and gets one free." Mrs. Brooks explained as she fought to keep from laughing.

"Are you serious?" I asked trying to keep a straight face.

"What's going on, Bobby?" I asked with my serious parental expression.

"Grandmother brought me a lot of candy bars so I put them in my book bag and brought them to school to make a deal."

Holding back a laugh, I told the teacher I would handle the situation, and thanked her for letting me know. On the way home, Bobby looked at me like he did not understand the problem. I looked back at him and just smiled. Eventually, I explained to him that he couldn't open a business at school. It was obvious he did not understand the business end of things. He was just making kids happy.

By the time Bobby got to high school, he had absorbed the total philosophy his grandmother instilled in him. He was a royal prince and the secret was in giving. She had taught him that giving answers all things and it was the answer to every problem. So, not only was he a royal prince, he was one with a big heart.

One day I pulled up in our drive way to go in the house and saw Bobby's complete brand new bedroom suit disassembled and sitting on our front porch mattresses and all. I'm looking at it but I can't believe it.

"Bobby, why is this furniture out here on the porch?"

"We were in class today and our teacher was telling us about families from another country not having beds to sleep in so I wanted to help. They can have my bed."

"What are you going to sleep on?"

"I can sleep on the floor. It doesn't matter to me." Bobby said as he turned and walked back in the house.

"I bought that furniture." I said.

"For me and this is what I want to do with it."

He was in the ninth grade then. I shook my head and surrendered to the cause. That was not enough. In that same year, he begged me to let his cousin have his car because she was pregnant with a family with no transportation.

"Mom, we have three cars. Can Pea Bea have my car? I can catch the bus to school."

"You can't be the answer to everybody's problem, Bobby. I just bought that car."

"I'll pay you back for it. I'm working now." Bobby said.

"You can give her the car if she agrees to make payments on it," I told him.

Everything was going along fine. Bobby was enjoying learning gymnastics. He was fascinating his instructors. He was doing the impossible. One evening during practice, he took off into the air and jumped so high in the air people watched with their jaws hanging down. It was a phenomenal jump, except this particular time his mind and body did not connect to tell him to land on his feet.

Taking a me-time, I was strolling down the isles of Wal-Mart when I received a call on my cell phone. It was from Bobby's high school girlfriend.

"Mrs. Wattley, this is Michelle. They are taking Bobby to the hospital."

"What happened?"

"He didn't bend. He just fell... dropped out of the air!"

I ran out of Wal-Mart and jumped into my car. Looking up to the sky, I prayed to God that my son would be alright and I prayed for strength to travel across town to get to the hospital. I got to the hospital and the prognosis revealed that he may have damaged his liver and might be paralyzed.

I entered the room to see Bobby. They had him immobile. I told him he would be fine and waited for all the tests to come back. My son was able to walk out the hospital that same night. Hallelujah!

One thing both my sons inherited from their father is athletic ability. I remember watching Robert play football. I was amazed at his abilities; his style was captivating. I knew what I saw but to hear it from the men and the women who witnessed it as well was very special.

"You know Mrs. Wattley that boy can go far with that football. I look forward to watching him play every game. He is so entertaining!"

"Thank you." I said.

"Robert was running all over that field. I have never seen one player tackle him," another person said.

One day I was over my mother's house and my brother stopped by with the newspaper in his hand. He was hyped up and eager to talk about his nephew.

"Lyn, you know he can go pro. I can't believe he is outrunning Copley's star player. Look every week I read the paper and Bink is carrying the ball less but covering more yards. That boy is a fast and a strong runner."

"Yeah, I've been hearing good things about him." I said.

The next football game was an awesome game for him. It also was his first injury. He tore the ligaments in his knee and had to have surgery. When the doctor told him he would need surgery, he put his head down and asked to go talk with his granddaddy. My father was a man he trusted and respected. My father encouraged him to have the surgery so he had the surgery. Even after surgery and limping on crutches, he sat on the bench at all the games. Feeling a need to get back on the field, he went extra miles to strengthen his knee. The doctor told him after about six weeks he could play football but he would have to wear a brace.

I remember his determination to play hard and well as he ran up and down the football field with his brace on. Of course he stopped wearing it and jumped into the game like he never had surgery and continued to have an outstanding season. He graduated and moved out of the house. It was then I learned Robert had received hundreds of opportunities to play football at various colleges but hid them from me.

He eventually told me he was not going to leave his baby brother. He did not want him to go through what he went through. He had no one in front of him to tell him what it meant to be a man. That year Robert made sure Marcus had the best of everything from cleats for football to a nice car. Wherever Marcus was, his big brother was there.

Through all the experiences I had with my son, car accidents were ongoing. I went to the scene of one of his accidents. He was standing beside his car with the most pleasant smile on his face.

"Mom, it wasn't my fault," Robert told me.

"Are you alright?" I said while I looked him over to see if he suffered any injuries.

"Yeah, I am fine. I really didn't do anything."

"We'll get attorney Wilson on this." I said reassuring him I believed his story of the accident.

In the meantime, I am talking to Robert looking at his nice Oldsmobile propped up on a telephone pole like an airplane, totaled. I was thanking God for sparing his life. Hallelujah!

Robert decided to join the National Guard. The army had always been an attraction to him. Although, I preferred he would never join. I was exhaling now. Both my sons were graduated from high school and they were now attending college. Then, it happened. My life changed forever.

"Mom, my unit came down to go to Iraq."

"You can't go. Your shoulder is separated. No way and it is your left arm, your shooting arm. You can't go!"

A year had gone by and the unit had not gone to Iraq. Although people felt it was a good sign, God had revealed to me that my son was going to Iraq. I became very quiet, as people expected for me to be excited. I was consecrating my self with God.

"Mom, we're going." Robert said.

"I know." I told him.

"You know it don't take Iraq for me to die. I can die falling down these steps."

Robert said as he walked down our upstairs steps with a smile on his face.

"I know, Robert. But if you had not messed up your shoulder playing that crazy football game with your working buddies, I would feel a lot better about it. You're left handed. That's your best arm."

"How are you going to carry all that weight with that shoulder all messed up?" I asked as if it would make him consider not going.

"I'll be alright. I have to be there for my unit. I have to do what I have to do."

While in Iraq, God spoke in my spirit "*I got him.*" I did not have to worry. There were times the spirit would awaken me in the middle of the night and tell me to get on the computer. Robert would be there having a rough time. Easter Sunday, I knew God was on the throne. He awakened me and this is what He told me:

"*I got him. Start praying, they are in danger.*"

My phone rang three times, One was my mother, two my stepmother and three, my friend, Louanne. We all felt a need to pray for Robert and his platoon at the same time. Upon praying, I was led to turn on my television. There was a convoy that had been ambushed by insurgents. They were outnumbered tremendously. The odds were, they wouldn't make it. When I saw the truck, I knew my son was connected to it.

God blessed him to call home to let us know he was alright. Hallelujah!

In time, he shared with me that he was the first soldier to fire back at the enemy. He received a medal for his performance. If he had not fired back, that convoy might have been killed.

"Mom, it was so natural for me to shoot back. I didn't have to think about it. I just did it."

Though my son was in Iraq, he was able to bless people in the states. Mother's Day me, and all three of his grandmothers received a dozen roses and a stuffed animal. His brother did not have to want for anything either. A woman struggling to pay bills was blessed by him; donations to our church, his car went to a minister. My mom was surprised when the UPS truck pulled up in her drive way carrying a new micro wave. He kept giving and sending.

Robert has always been the bee in my bonnet because he had such a big heart. He did not try to please me; he only loved me and demanded I loved him as God had made him. Embracing his grandmother's philosophy, *The Secret is in Giving*, He constantly gives to people as though it was his last day on earth. I guess I kept waiting for him to do something for me that he would not do for others. It never happened. He always gives his all and his best to everybody.

Like Mary, I had to learn to give up my son that the world may continue to be blessed. Mary and I also learned the greatest presence in life is their Father, God, Almighty. For this, I will eternally be grateful for my bundle of joy, RDW III, the man of God with a heart of Gold. Robert's famous words are:

"Going to church don't make you a Christian no more than going to McDonald's making you a hamburger. You have to live it."

Linda D. Wattley is the author of a healing trilogy revealing the truth about sexual abuse. Her newest release, "Something About an Angel" is the first installment of this trilogy followed with "Deeper Than Love" and "This Thing Called Love". Wattley will be debuting two self-help books this year, "Last Day of Victimization" and "I know Mixed Signal Syndrome". Her goal is to offer spiritual and mental support to victims all over the world.

Contact Linda at: email: <u>universalove26@yahoo.com</u>

What Did I do

By: Apostle Tracey George

Throughout most of my childhood, I was the 'do-gooder'. In any case, that was what people called me. At the age of five, with no real knowledge of what I was doing, one of God's gifts made its first appearance in my life. I had my little friends line-up on the porch and they tarried for the Holy Spirit.... I actually worked with them. I talked them through the process and stood there with tissue and wiped there tiny mouths as they called out to God. I was adamant about their salvation even though I did not fully understand what salvation was all about. My mother took notice of us and came to the door. She told us to go play. Later, she initiated my education in the things of God. At that moment I truly felt that the Lord was ready to use me; it was time. Many believe that children do not have wilderness experiences or that God would not allow a child to go through. For me, that is when it all began....

It was the summer of 1977 and school was out. Here I was the tall and skinny kid from Florida ready to seize the opportunity to travel. I said goodbye to friends and prepared for the big road trip to visit relatives. Everything was lovely at first when we arrived at my grandparent's home. We joked; even shared stories. Then my parents left us there for a month and a half. While there, I became acquainted with a completely different lifestyle. I discovered that folks gossiped about children just as fervently as they would a grown person. Name-calling was the order of the day back then. Often I thought to myself, *aren't these people churchgoers*. My grandfather tried to do what he could to protect me from all of that; however, I was frequently the topic for the day... Often times we do not realize the trauma one can face as a child when dealing with physical and emotional abuse. It was awful. I began to realize that I did not fit in. One family member locked me out

141

of the house and chased me around the yard with a switch. He knew I was scared of the dog that was in the yard, yet he did not stop. I had never experienced mistreatment of that magnitude. *Why were thy picking on me?* It may seem normal to some but to me it was very strange. My parents did not raise me that way. They taught us to respect others and to fear God. I would go into the bathroom and lock the door. In there I would question God. *Why was this happening to me? I did not bother anybody.*

Before the trip, I was an honor student. I enjoyed reading books. I loved school. I liked to play, but reading was at the top of the list for me. There were days when the relatives wanted us to go outside and play. Well I preferred to stay inside and read. Often ridiculed for this and forced to go play, I received many beatings. My brother tried to stand up for me but it only cost him. Soon, I began to withdraw. I had taken enough emotionally and physically. I tried to recall scriptures or anything that would help me deal with the drama and move on. I heard sermons on faith as a child yet had no clue that God was taking me through my own personal journey of faith. This journey would challenge me and push me beyond what I considered humanly possible. God told us in James that faith without works is dead. For me, this scripture represented why God raised me up the way He did. He showed me that I would have to go through, even during childhood. By the time my parents came to pick us up, I was a completely different child. Initially, I was outspoken and a 'ham', now I did not say much at all. Little did I know this would be the start of a long struggle with depression. Although I was not molested in the home of my relatives, I was emotionally and physically abused... I shared this information with no one. I conveniently forgot the incidents of that summer; at least I tried. I went back to school as if nothing happened. As time went on, I became more withdrawn. At the age of eleven, we moved to the same city where everything had transpired. Our family joined the same church. That year I invited God into my life and enjoyed the identical experience that I had seen in the adults. Later on, I became a junior altar evangelist; still, I had no idea what the Lord had in store. I began the process of ministering while wounded. At sixteen, I heard the Lord's voice concerning ministry and my involvement. He informed me that I was going to preach His word.

For the next ten years, I continued to sneak messages in wherever I could. I spoke at seminars, to introduce songs for the choir and during testimony services. With all of this going on, I quietly battled with depression. Though I was acquainted with many, I had few friends. It was in those years that I became a recluse. I sat in my room for hours reading the Bible or novels. That was my escape.

Eventually, I remembered what happened to me all of those years ago. I had suppressed it. Once it came back to mind, I began to hate those that had anything to do with what took place. One day my brother called and told my mother that she needed to talk to me about the events that took place the summer of 1977. That was the first time I spoke about it. My mother tried to encourage me through the word of God and to remind me of my faith in Him. Once again, I thought that I had fixed the problem. I questioned why it had to happen to me. I was only eight years old. I continued to hate the people who had hurt me and I remained depressed. Now I was in college and the tension only increased; I could not take it anymore. At that time, I was in college and in the army reserves and I had the church mask on; pretending that everything was all right.

Thoughts of suicide invaded my mind all the time. I went to a college professor and asked her in a round about way if she knew what was wrong with 'my friend'. She informed me that 'my friend' was possibly borderline manic-depressive. I kept the information to myself. I continued to disguise the problem. One day my mother took me to school and told me that the Lord said I needed to deal with the depression. I tried, but I was not successful.

I married and continued to pursue my education while miserable. Time passed on and I became pregnant with my son. I was happy to be pregnant yet sad that my son would soon enter a world filled with darkness and confusion. The tension of time and things out of control got the best of me and I attempted to take my life. In my bedroom, I heard a voice say now is the time, no one cares for you and you have carried all that mess long enough. It continued to press me by stating that I was bringing my child into a world full of hate and reminded me of all the mess I had suffered as a kid. I decided to listen. I took a glass of orange juice that I had been drinking and poured ammonia in it until it reached the rim. I took a sip of it; I opened my mouth to gulp the rest. My husband tried to open the door; it was locked. He had to force the door open. The scent of ammonia was so strong that he had to open the windows and doors to allow the air to flow. I stood there dumbfounded; I had snapped.

One of the myths that we must dispel is that everything is lovely after you have an encounter with God. Many come to God and believe that they will have no more problems. That is not true! When I attempted suicide, I was grown yet still dealing with demons from yesteryear. This was a part of the process. I had to endure. Time passed and I finally had to deal with the mess that had become my life so I could move on to the next phase of my life.

I graduated from college and prepared to embark on the new challenges this elevation would bring. I was moving forth in the things of God and considered the previous oppositions as opportunities to share with others how God will keep you even when you are not able to keep yourself. My husband and I tagged teamed for my first official sermon. Finally, I felt as if the battles were over and now it would be smooth sailing. Our son was 2 years old when we left South Carolina and headed to Texas. We arrived in Texas prepared to start a new life together as a family and in ministry. I signed in at Fort Hood to prepare for the start of my military time there. All was great. I met my coworkers and my family found a home. There were no troubles! We even located a place of Worship. During my time at Ft Hood, after eleven years in the military, I got out and had my second child. Little did I know that life was getting ready to change.

And David fled from Naioth in Ramah, and came and said before Jonathan. What have I done? What is mine iniquity? And what is my sin before thy father, that he seeketh my life? (1 Samuel 20:1)

Everything was going fine and then I found myself in a spiritual whirlwind. Life was at an all time high. Aint no stopping us now, until.... We were stopped. All of a sudden, things changed. Everything crashed. Life completely flip-flopped. Those that were for me were now against me and I did not understand why? If that was not enough, the job was gone, the marriage had ended and I was over a thousand miles away from home. Here I am a military veteran, a minister of the gospel singing and preaching His praises, and a mother of two yet hell found its way into my house. This is not supposed to be happening so I thought. In addition to the storm, some of my mentors were chasing me; I found out that the 'Saul's' in my life only wanted to use and not train me. I discovered that foolishness did not only exist in the pews but in the pulpit also. God exposed so many things to me that I attempted to close my eyes and hoped He would choose another. Depression attempted to rear its head yet again but I was ready... This time I knew what to do. I had been here before; I dealt with that demon previously. I knew I had to get a grip before it had a chance to mess with me. I pulled out the heavy artillery and told depression goodbye in Jesus name. I began to rejoice about it! Finally, for the first time, I was free from hopelessness. I

145

had no more drama and withdrawals. I even shared the testimony with many. Then things changed again... I remember it as if it were yesterday... The Lord spoke so clear. He told me to get ready; I was going to go through a wilderness season. He never stated the exact date nor did He say when it would be over.... He just said get ready. *Get ready for another wilderness?* Before becoming irate, I researched the wilderness and its precise meaning.

The wilderness according to Webster is an unsophisticated and abandoned place. Right away, I knew I would be unaccompanied on this 'journey'; I could not take anybody with me. In order to minister God's word effectively, I had to weather the storms. That sounded good yet I thought that it was a mistake. All hell was breaking lose and it had nothing to do with the devil! In addition to the announcement, the Lord informed me that I had to continue to minister the gospel and be joyful in relation to it. This hurt me bad. I wanted to crawl under a rock and wait for the storm to blow over. I had been through a sufficient amount of mayhem... I had my tempest as a child. Did that not count for anything I thought, *Oh, Lord! I did not ask for this. Why is this happening to me? Have I not been faithful Lord?* The Lord expected me to keep on ministering to others even as I went through. Countless days I ministered with tears hidden behind my eyes. I remember sitting on my couch wondering when God was going to come through for me. When would things turn around? Yet, He said nothing. Constantly, I examined scriptures I had learned as a kid growing up in church. *Behold I have refined thee, but not with silver; I have chosen thee in the furnace of affliction. For mine own sake, even for mine own sake, will I do it: for how should my name be polluted? and I will not give my glory unto another.* (Isaiah 48: 10-11)

Romans 8:18 *For I consider that the sufferings of this present time are not worthy to be compared with the glory which shall be REVEALED IN US.*

Still nothing prepared me for the hurdles I faced. I called my mother trying to find the answers. I questioned God. I began to ask Him where I missed it. What was wrong with me? What did I do to warrant such treatment? The conclusion, I had a problem. I went on a fast in order to get an answer from God. You name it I did it... to fix my condition. I assumed that God was too merciful and kind to allow His children to go through such chaos. I thought.... I must have done something terribly wrong. I will go to God and He will forgive me of the sin committed. Like Job's Friends, I inquired. *Did I do anything that would cause God to be mad at me?* I wanted this to be over and I did everything I could think of to rid my children and me of this. I repented repeatedly for everything I could think of. I even contemplated the possibility that I was reaping something sown. I was having a hard time accepting the fact that this wilderness was an important part of the journey I had to go through. The Lord encouraged me to read about Joseph. In Genesis 37, The Lord showed me that Joseph had gone through something similar. He was his father's favorite. Additionally, his being favored caused his brothers to hate him with a passion. In spite of all of that, the Lord gave him several visions. Each vision depicted what the future had in store. His brothers became furious with him; they conspired to slay him. One of his brothers, Reuben, intervened. In verse 22 of the same chapter, His brother declared that they should throw him into the pit. His brothers stripped him of his coat and cast him into the pit. With that alone, I could relate. Many of us have had to face the fury of another. I finally discovered that it was nothing personal; this would be a time of self-discovery and awareness...

As the story goes on, his cousins the Ishmeelites showed up; some Midianites got him out of the pit and sold him to them. From there Joseph ended up in Egypt at Potiphar's home. Through it all Joseph remained faithful and God gave him favor. While in Egypt, he was accused of rape and thrown into prison. He continued to go through yet God continued to give him favor. Each situation was a challenge but God delivered. What about you have you questioned God? Have you found yourself in the same predicaments? Constantly wondering why things happen to you and when will they stop? You are not alone. David asked Jonathan a similar question... "What have I done?" Saul (Jonathan's Father) had tried to kill David unsuccessfully. What I had to understand was God had brought David to this place. He anointed him to be King and regardless of what anybody else thought God made the final decision (Proverbs 16:33). He took him into his home and the moment the anointing on his life was visible, he began to pursue him. Saul, driven by his jealousy continued to hunt David yet God had a plan. David left his father's home and moved in with the king. He did not know the women would exclaim his victories so loudly. In spite of all of this, God sent him to the king's home. This was a part of his destiny; little did he know that every hurdle was actually pushing him towards his calling, through his wilderness experience. The purpose of the wilderness was to process me/ to prepare me for occupation. When you come out of the wilderness, you come out to possess the land. We believe we already have what it takes to possess it; yet, we find out that we must go through the fire in order to come out as pure gold.

While in the wilderness, I discovered my destiny (destiny is one's preordained future, their inner purpose), I encountered God in a way that is unique to any other occurrence. Soon we sat together as He pointed out some of the things he had purposed for my life. He showed me that truly he had been with me the entire time. He never left. He was there while I suffered as a child and through every obstacle as an adult. Praise God! God reminded me of David's story. Like David, I had been through much yet it was not in vain. God had a divine plan. I had to realize that the spears thrown could not kill me. Even with the spears thrown, God gave David the ability to duck! Thank you Lord, we do not have to sit idly by and allow ourselves to be struck instead we have an advocate in our Father! Yes, I had to duck many times. Nevertheless, God expressed to me that what I was going through had nothing to do with fault, rather future. God told me I had a lot to learn about storms and the wilderness. I had to face the fact that there was a purpose.   God had the blueprint for my life in His mind. However, the thing about destiny... you have to journey through some hurdles to get there. This journey may include valleys, mountains, storms, or deserts.   I realized that none of it was there to stop me; however, they were to propel me in to what He had for me all along. During the wilderness, my flesh went through to the point of death.   Through obedience, He replaced the old heart with a new one. This new heart is full of compassion for the things that matter to Him. When you come out of your wilderness correctly, passion will overflow. The extraordinary thing about all of this is that God replaces your heart so you do not walk away with a foul attitude. You will have a different outlook on life, a fresh perspective.   As for me, I no longer hate.   I have forgiven those that mistreated me and I have conquered that which tried to conquer me. It took God's word to make it. He always reminded me that I was on the earth for a reason. What is your destiny? What is God's plan for your life?   Frequently we spend so much time looking at the difficulty with out considering the fact that God has already ordered our steps. I had to learn that truth for myself. Sometimes our steps lead us through valleys we cannot explain. God wants to comfort your heart to let you know that He is in control even when it does seem like it. Rest in Him and know that it is not about you; it is about Him. Cast all of your cares on

Him. He truly will remain faithful and comfort you as you journey through to the end.

Apostle Tracey George, Sr Pastor/Founder of the Core Outreach Network was born in Eglin Air Force Base, Florida to Pastors Kent and Ruby George (Sanctuary Pastors for The Citizens of the King). **Apostle George has two children** Kenneth and Nitara. In addition to being a mother, **Apostle George** is a writer, vocalist, comedian, songwriter, motivational speaker, counselor, and spoken word artist.

Contact Apostle Tracey at: email: puregold4christ@yahoo.com

Due Season

By: Minister Kim Y. Jackson

Every Christian can be assured that throughout their lifetime, they will go through seasons. This is confirmed in God's word in Ecclesiastes 3:1 which declares, "There is a time for everything and a season for everything under heaven." Throughout the Bible God refers to specific seasons in the life of His people to show the expected end that He has promised each of us, performed by His sovereign will. The Seasons depicted in the Old and New Testament were written to commemorate explicit moments in the lives of God's people to encourage the generations to come, to know that God alone enables His children to remain steadfast, overcome insurmountable odds, be restored, receive unexpected blessings, become empowered and remain faithful to the calling that He has predestined for us from the beginning of time. Every one of the spiritual symbols revealed in each story about the seasons of the lives of His people shows the mercy and love of God for them.

God allowed me to experience seasons of weeping, seasons of joy, a time of breaking down, a time of healing, a time of silence, as well as a time to speak. While going through these seasons He walked me into the beginning and through the end of the season and showed me the purpose of each one. Walking in Faith through each season I saw God's preordained plan for my life. He even showed me that there is a specific spiritual significance for my "Due Season." Therefore, my brothers and sisters for whatever season you are in at this very moment you can be assured that "God knows the plans that He has for you," Jeremiah 29:11 and He also knows that there is a Due Season predestined for your life to proclaim His Glory.

While participating in a heightened worship experience in church one Sunday, I heard the Spirit of the Lord say *"I will release my Latter Rain in Due Season."* I was instantly overjoyed and awestruck all at the same time. Though I am use to hearing God's voice, this time the voice and the words I heard were bolder and more pronounced. To hear the still sweet voice of the Lord has always been a privilege to me and I never take hearing His voice for granted. The words that were spoken *Due Season*, resounded in my spirit over and over again. When I heard these words I felt that my current season was coming to an end, the current assignment was complete and the Lord was releasing me into a new place of promise. In our Due Season the lessons that need to be learned are accomplished, the sacrifices that are required are done and the level of faith that God had preordained for us to walk in, becomes fully realized. Hearing the words Due Season spoken by the Spirit of the Lord took me to a new place in faith of the power of our Lord and Savior Jesus Christ. Hallelujah.

At the end of the same worship service where I heard the Holy Spirit say *"I will release my Latter Rain in Due Season,"* I also heard another declaration from the Lord saying, *"This is Due Season."* Once again, I became overwhelmed at the King of Kings for revealing His will and revealing it before me. First God said that "He will release His Latter Rain in Due Season" and now He is saying that at this present time in my life, "It is Due Season." Hearing these words were more than my heart could take. They were like a symphony that took my breath away. These beautiful words became my source of contentment and peace. I had done nothing to deserve God speaking these words. Nor could I determine a reason for why God would allow me to hear these words. I knew that it was for His Glory and that is exactly what I did. I glorified, praised and worshipped Him for this mighty act He had allowed me to witness.

In my Due Season I now see another dimension of God, called the "Latter Rain." It is the outpouring of God, released into the hands of His children. This is the time established whereby God,

152

has set before you an open door, and no one can shut it, Revelations 3:8.

Shortly after hearing these beautiful words from the Lord, I was reviewing my emails and I saw an announcement seeking authors to contribute to an anthology entitled, "This Far by Faith." I knew that the Lord had commissioned me to write on His behalf and it was His job to complete the preparation required for me to do this essential work to build His Kingdom. Through the Holy Spirit I recognized that this was the time He prepared me for. This is the "Latter Rain" God had promised and it had come in its "Due Season." Previously, I attempted to perform works for the Lord and moved before Him. Growing through these experiences I realized that I had to "Wait on the Lord; Be of good courage", according to Psalm 27:14. However, now is the designated time for my Due Season to use my God given gifts and walk in faith, for the Glory of God to be shown through me. I stepped out in Faith, believing God to do this work through me, and I answered the announcement to submit a written work for the anthology. Then God released His omnipotent power during my Due Season to get the work done.

In the Latter Rain there is nothing required of you but to move forward in faith. God does it all, shows you the resources, opens the doors and says to you through His Holy Spirit, *"Go forth in My name."* Yes, He also said this to me during my preparation towards "Due Season." Upon hearing these words I recognized that there was nothing that I could possibly due to accomplish this or any other task for God. Now I had finally released God to do the work through me, without my help. I am grateful to God for giving me His word though His Holy Spirit and for bringing me to the place where I am no longer comfortable being dependent on my abilities, but seek to be solely dependent on Him.

In preparation for my Due Season the Lord gently guided me to walk in Faith, gave me words of Faith for encouragement, perfected me for seasons yet to come, converted the old man to the new man, showed me the affect of time on His perfect will and revealed He had predestined me and then brought me into my Due Season. Each of these steps is depicted herein to direct you into your Due Season.

Faith for Due Season

In my walks of Faith, I experienced seasons I thought would never end. In other seasons I endured, I thought I would never survive. Yet for the cause of Christ I remained faithful to the belief that the power of God would prevail. Throughout these seasons I cried a lot and used lots of tissue. Interestingly enough, while going through seasons with the Lord I encountered many Christians who could not fully comprehend the power of God that I knew or experienced. Some questioned my decisions and others opposed the paths that I followed. Without question I knew the paths I was taking were directed by the Lord. These same people couldn't conceptualize the obedience that was required of me which was preparing me for my "Due Season." I often saw questions on their faces and heard the words that were never spoken like, "Why are you experiencing these hardships and following these unusual paths?" But I knew God was building up a greater measure of Faith in me for my "Due Season." During these times of preparation and testing, I was drawn to follow the leading of the Holy Spirit and not man. It became apparent to me that all the while the Lord was holding me in the hollow of His hand and He wanted me to walk in Faith towards my Due Season. Walking in faith was never designed to be seen through the natural eye. It is more for the believer in Christ to trust the invisible God of all creation.

Words of Faith for Due Season

Chosen to walk this path of Faith with God, He gave me a scripture to stand on to help me reach my Due Season. He knew there would be times of extreme testing and wanted to give me personal words of strength to endure this part of my journey. Romans 4:20-21, states, "He did not waiver at the promise of God through unbelief, but was strengthened in faith, giving Glory to God, and being fully convinced that what He had promised, He was also able to perform. These words are my "orders" to walk in Faith, to endure, stand and press forward towards my "Due Season." God's word in Romans 4:20 speaks of the characteristics of perseverance instilled within Abraham, while he waited for God to fulfill His promises. The Holy Spirit showed me in this scripture the development of Abraham's ability to be firm in his convictions of His belief in God, the process he undertook to be strengthened in faith, how he extolled to all mankind the magnificent splendor and majesty of God personified, as he was fully convinced of God's sovereign ability. This scripture repeatedly encourages me to continue to press through the many seasons of life that I walk with the Lord. These are the words of encouragement that I speak over my life often. God has given me other scriptures to add to these words of encouragement and strength found in Romans 4:20-21. However, there are no other words but these that have personally kept me rooted along the journey towards my Due Season.

God gives each of His children a specific word to carry us through the journey of every season, but we must be listening for and obedient to the word He gives us. God's word is filled with power and is all consuming to those who trust and believe in it. As we acknowledge, accept and move in the power of His word, we must also be willing to acknowledge, accept and submit to His will for the seasons of our lives.

155

God's Perfecting Will for Due Season

God's will for all of His children is manifested in many seasons and is designed to perfect us. Matthew 26:39 declares, "Not my will, but thy will be done." For the Christian who has their own agenda and continues to hold on to their own capabilities, this will be one of the hardest seasons and a season of the utmost importance as you proceed towards your "Due Season." The reason why this is one of the hardest seasons is because it is the season of your surrender to God's perfecting will. Just so you know, this was my hardest season. God was breaking off my carnal nature of thinking, to transform my mind. He admonished me to "walk in the spirit and not to fulfill the lust of the flesh" (Galatians 5:1) for my "Due Season." A negative mindset, reasoning not guided by the Holy Spirit and gravitation towards ungodly perspectives have now been replaced by the activation of taking on the mind of Christ to help me walk steady in Faith, on the course to my "Due Season." The scriptures tell us to "Be ye transformed by the renewing of your mind" (Romans 12:2). I honestly believe that the renewing of my mind was one of the best works God conducted within me. God's goal continues to be transforming me so that His perfect will is done in my life and my mind. He did this so that I would be prepared for my new life in my "Due Season."

As I submitted to the will of God, I was able to see the transformation of my will into His will, right before my eyes. The Holy One of Israel had an alternative plan to mine. Going through this season, I couldn't conceive the mercy's of God acting on my behalf for His sovereign will to be done. During this time I felt like every plan placed before me was unfair. I quickly learned that His perfecting will for this season was a spiritual transformation of the mind and He would get it done by any means necessary.

Conversion for Due Season

Knowing that there had to be a purpose for this season, I decided to embrace God's ability to know all, be all and to do all. This season was designed to help me see God and His ability to convert my heart and mind, in preparation for my "Due Season." There were seasons of loneliness where all of my loved ones were separated from me. Thoughts of being alone during the heat of my trials drove me closer to God to seek His love, comfort, companionship, direction and opinions. In this season God was teaching me about intimacy with Him. The thoughts of loneliness were cast down when I embraced God's word that declared that "He would never leave me nor forsake me," Hebrews 13:5. There were seasons of financial hardships where all I knew was an abundance of lack. Surely, God had told me time and time again that He would supply all of my needs according to His riches in Glory, Philippians 4:19. At that time I was determined to be self-sufficient instead of God dependent. However, in this season, the Lord converted me from doing everything for myself and showed me that "He is able to do exceedingly and abundantly above all that we ask or think, according to the power that works in us," Ephesians 3:20.

During my season of conversion, it seemed that the more I cried out to the Lord, the more it seemed that He must not have been listening. Each time I felt this way God would gently remind me that He heard my faintest cry. From the natural eye I remember seeing so much that was being taken from me. The Lord began to reveal His word to me concerning this season in Psalms 37:25, "I have been young and now am old, Yet I have never seen the righteous forsaken nor His seed begging bread." Therefore, as a child of God I have everything that I need because His word says, "For My grace is sufficient for thee," (2Cor 12:9). He was also teaching me financial discipline for a season that was yet to come.

God's goal for me in this season was not to count the grain in the bags but to believe for the overflow.

In my early Christian walk God showed me that I would battle generational curses, self-imposed bondage and a host of spiritual strongholds designed to destroy me in the seasons of my life. In the heat of some battles I questioned whether those seasons were really part of the plan God had for me. In some of these circumstances I also began to question the true existence of God, knowing all the time that He is and will always be the creator of all creation. Through experiencing seasons of warfare, God revealed the warrior that He has called me to be and the ability He has placed within me to "Fight the good Fight of Faith", 2 Timothy 4:7, to carry me into my "Due Season." As a warrior in God's army, know that we are continuously trained for and during the heat of battle. It is interesting to see God convert so many dimensions of my life and it was all for my good.

Affects of time on "Due Season"

My seasons with the Lord often existed as endless moments in time. Minutes turned into hours, hours turned into days, days turned into months and some months turned into years. I found myself consumed by the question of why did my Due Season take so long? Realizing that the seasons I experienced with God had less to do with the duration of time and more to do with me submitting to the will of God, I stopped asking God about the duration of time. I was often told, "What you are going through is just for a season." I am so grateful that God watches over our seasons to make sure that the process He designed, to bring us to our Due Season is fulfilled. God the watchman of our souls calls us to and brings us through every season. My seasons with God are the paths that He wanted me to take for His namesake and not for the sake of time. I questioned whether I would ever come out

158

of some seasons long enough to catch my breath. To this He replied to me in Psalms 27:1-6, "For in the day of trouble He will keep me safe in His dwelling; He will hide me in the shelter of His tabernacle and set me high upon a rock." I thank God that His perfecting will is being done within His time frame. The duration of time is of no significance into bringing us into our "Due Season." Though we may want to count time during our circumstances, God's word in 2 Peter 3:8, states, "But do not forget this one thing, dear friends; With the Lord a day is like a thousand years, and a thousand years are like a day." Saints of God take heart in knowing that He is faithful to us in every endeavor that we undertake because it is in His plans and the time that we spend in preparation for our Due Season is necessary because it has been predestined by God.

Predestined for Due Season

Before God called forth His perfect creation [His children], He designed the purpose and strategy for the implementation of our "Due Season. God himself predetermined, prearranged, and preset the pathway for each of us to reach our "Due Season. To make sure that every Christian understands that God directs our steps, He gives us His word in Romans 8:30 that proclaims, "Those He predestined He also called, those He called He also justified, those He justified He also Glorified. This is God's response to any question we may have about His plan for our lives.

As I continue to walk in Faith towards my Due Season I am grateful for the assurance conveyed by Romans 8:30 for two reasons. First, there is nothing to take place in my life that God has not devised and allowed. Secondly, I was predestined to experience my "Due Season," as written in God's word. Throughout the bible there are many stories about God's children who walked in Faith into their "Due Season." There was Moses, who was predestined to lead Israel out of the hands of Pharaoh. Rahab the Harlot was predestined to lead spies into safety and be a part of the lineage of Jesus Christ. John the Baptist was predestined to prepare the way for Jesus the Messiah and through obediently baptizing Him, he witnessed the Glory of the Lord descend in a dove. Like so many other Christians from the Old and New Testaments God has plans that include our "Due Season." For we are predestined to do greater works in the Kingdom of God at its appointed "Due Season."

God's Glory in Due Season

As a Christian we must all trust that our Due Season is constructed to give God the Glory. The purpose of every work accomplished through the life of every Christian on God's behalf and the preparation required to complete the work is inevitably to give God the Glory. It is at that time that we show forth the splendor, magnificence and power of God. The world looks at the lives of Christians and often stands in judgment of us because of our past. So much so that they believe it is impossible for Christians to do anything other than what we are identified with from our past. But because of the Holy Spirit that dwells within us, God's children perform supernatural works for the entire world to see. It is here that the world witnesses the Glorify of God which is predestined for a specific significance in its "Due Season." What the world inevitably sees is the life changing power of Jesus Christ. The purpose is for the world to see that "The things that seem impossible with men are possible with God," Luke 18:27. Oh, how we do Glorify God for every "Due Season."

The revelation I received from hearing the words *Due Season* continues to overwhelm me. I acknowledge and embrace the fact that there are more "Due Seasons" to come. The word of God tells us in Philippians 1:6, "Being confident of this very thing, that He who has begun a good work in you will complete it until the day of Jesus Christ." Amen. The master plan for perfecting me to complete the work God called me to do shall never end. It is humbling to know that the purpose of my existence is coming to fulfillment, by walking in Faith and trusting in the Lord. What a wonderful God we serve. How can we say no to Him, once we fully realize the majesty and Glory of His sovereign will and power?

For every Christian that is seeking their Due Season recall that the word of God in Psalms 1:3 which declares, "*He shall be like a tree planted by the rivers of water that bringeth forth fruit in its season. His leaf also shall not wither and whatsoever He shall do shall prosper.*" This is the word of God declaring that every Christian shall have their "Due Season." God backs up His word once again in Galatians 6:9 stating, "in Due Season" you will reap if you faint not. Trust and believe in God's word. Embrace the time and process that He prepares you to come into your Due Season and seek after the will of God for you to complete your assignment in its "Due Season."

Minister Kim Y. Jackson, M. Divinity is an anointed writer, teacher, and oracle for the Lord. She has written three self-published books. Her works have been featured in Say So Magazine and the Maryland Women of Worship Devotional. Kim is the President of God's Glory Publishing Company and Wellspring of Living Waters consulting firm. Minister Kim encourages believers in Christ to write the vision that God has given them to follow. For more information please visit her web page at: writethevizn@aol.com or www.kimyjackson.com.

Such Is Life
By: Michelle Hardy

How do I know your word is bond, your hearts' sincere, your vow to me you say is on your life? You say you love me, you make love to me, in the heat of passion I am going to become your wife. But the mystery stands in every man, and the master plan remains behind the scene. You play the role, you act the part you say this is nice, but in the end you become my worst friend no more passion, no more dreams, it abruptly ends…

Such is Life…

My heart you steal, my soul you share, my love you desire when convenient and not in your way. You come and go as you please my feelings you tease, I no longer function on my own. I surrender my mind, my body, and my soul to you every day. You have your moments you have your timing and you know just how, where, and when to take me there. You keep me captive imprison my inner being and abusively somehow convince me that you truly care…

Such is Life…

You are a real man? You know what's best for me and your insults and decisions I hold them dear. You would not hurt me? You would not neglect me and my life surely you would not take with your own hands. My breath shortens, my heart races, and my life revisits the fear in every moment of anger you release. It's my fault; I don't deserve you, can't do better than you and better be grateful you even want me near…

Such is Life…

My mind is open, my spirit broken; my body is flushed of all joy. Let you tell it, I'm not a woman I am not human, I am just a toy. You toss me around, give me a permanent frown, and no matter what keep me so low I will never know. I am not to be beaten, I am not to be molested, I am not to be sold, or verbally

162

abused and wrongfully spoken too. You are not my maker, you are by no means my King and I am worth more than you lead me to believe...

Such is Life...

You are a beast not a man you desire to hold me down but not my hand. You release the venom that destroys my every need and disallow me my right to be a queen. To be me is unheard of I have no right to hold my head high and breath. You bring down my self esteem and hold back my true beauty and deny me the opportunity to be the blessing I am meant to be. I am stronger than you dictate to me, I am valuable and desirable and a real man's treasure I am; and that you continuously refuse to reveal to me...

Such is Life...

My day has come, I have been set free, and you no longer hold the key. I remove my shackles and dismiss the binding words you use to restrain and mentally abuse me. I am a flower, I am beauty in the light, and I no longer submit to tears throughout the night. I have found peace and my eyes are open to love and the real light. I have gained my heart back and my dignity I am woman and my intelligence and eagerness I hold on to so tight.

I know that I am a powerful being and you are just afraid of what I might...so you see my dear you uneducated, insufficient, insecure, poor excuse for a man. I am a Nubian queen a strong black man's dream. I know my strength and I am full of power. I am WOMAN; the gift God gave to man. With FAITH in the Master's plan, I will be alright. I am spirit filled and forgiving.

Such is life...

***Furious* FAITH**

By: Michelle Hardy

"Perception *(an attitude or understanding based on what is observed or thought)* is everything." How people see you, how you present yourself and your first impression is how you are remembered or seen thereafter. The clothes you wear, the car you drive, the neighborhood you live in, the way you walk, the way you talk, and the company that you keep; all determine your character and your values in the eyes of the world.

In my world it was dark and isolated as to not reveal a trace of drama in my life. It was absolutely unheard of and no way were my issues ever to be disclosed or displayed for others to see. I had a reputation to maintain. I thought I had a good life no way I was going to have anyone think less of me. Little did I know that my own deception was a major reflection of what I was going through and the whole world knew I was bitter and broken, but me.

"Deception *(an act, trick, or device intended to deceive somebody)* is betrayal. What seems good on the outside is not always good on the inside. I no longer ruled over my emotions and feelings. I knew love and relationships to be controlling, demanding, and abusive. These characteristics allowed me to be captive, damaged, and broken. I had no self-esteem, no drive, and no voice of my own but I was "in love." I believe I would not amount to anything and that I was a waste of his time. He told me I was less of a woman, damaged goods, and should be grateful to have him in my life; and I should make the best of his valuable but limited time. Verbally, I was belittled, beat down, and buried alive in disgrace and disgust.

My spirit said "no" and my flesh said "yes" to the never-ending domination I endured from day to day. I began to think I was losing my mind. That I was forbidden to be happy and that God

164

was punishing me for unmentionable behavior in my past. I was no angel, my skeletons I hid well. But surely, I was not to live in darkness for the rest of my life. I was guilty; my head hung low, my eyes filled with fear and tears streamed down my face like a never ending river of pain. Mentally, I had no power, my thoughts were under his control and I lived for him and him alone. "I loved him."

My first black eye; I convinced myself that it was my fault. I had to learn to shut my mouth, follow the rules of his house. I was not to stand up for what I knew was right. Even though, his intoxicated episodes led to his absence in the home multiple nights. He is a grown man and what he says is law. That was that; follow the rules and there would be one less argument; one less bruising fight. It was normal to be strong held, pushed around, and broken down. Memories of the horrible fights and the days of neglect were routine and I learned to overlook the hurt and the pain because I loved him.

Abuse *(defamation)* is controlling, overbearing, and reflects hidden emotion.

Verbal, mental, and physical abuse are a demonstration of low self-esteem and a need to have authority. How much do I take? How much more exploitation do I accept as the norm? Do I really have to fight this hard to be loved, is this the only way to love and be loved? The only way he could get over his hidden secrets, his inner nightmares, and the pain and fear he couldn't face on his own. So he had to place the blame for his bitterness on me. The more he drank the more darkness surrounded our relationship at all times and it became a part of my normal routine to accept the fact that there was no light at the end, and joy would never come in the morning.

The devil is a liar…

New foundation, shutting the door on the past, and walking away. These were the tools and the guidance God provided me through his word and the Holy Spirit that gave me the strength to call off my wedding, move out, and walk away. We no longer shared our lives I was seeking the kingdom of God and through his grace and his mercy, I found my identity, he set me free and I could now be me.

But, my lack of faith in God's grace left an open space and in my weaknesses; dark and full of doubt once again the enemy had his way. I had found my resting place I was in God's presence (I thought) but I was straddling the fence and wandered off and away. I had to have this man's love; I couldn't lose this *"gift from God."* I couldn't give up six years of disrespect, denial, and disgrace. I could love him and love God; he would change if I just hung in there.

July 23, 2007 the day after my birthday; the morning of my emergency reconstructive procedure, the orthopedic surgeon stood on the side of my bed explaining to me how my right foot hung from my leg by mere skin. How four hours of labor and determination would allow me at some point and time in the near future to walk again. The surgeon told me of the steel plate containing six screws he placed within to hold my foot, my ankle and my leg all together again. I thought it was the drugs, the anesthesia had me hallucinating and maybe even this was just one horrible nightmare. Oh no! When I woke up that same evening I realized I was in Kettering hospital, and a spirit of abuse had placed me there.

I cried deeply, so hard my body ached not only from the physical trauma and the surgery, but fatigue had settled in and I was broken and fed up. I cried out to God furiously and pleaded for his forgiveness and for Him to allow me to come home. He said to me "you are my child and in my presence you will always have a place." God says in **Joshua 1:5** *I will never leave you nor forsake you.* God was always there. He let me go through, he broke me down, "literally" to teach me obedience and show me

166

that his shielding, unconditional, unchanging, understanding, and merciful love is above all. Victory in Christ Jesus is the greatest relationship you can ever experience in a lifetime. I walk with him; I talk with him and I share my every thought and personal desires with him.

"I Got a Man"

He holds me oh so gentle, but firmly comforts me in my desperate times of great need.

He wipes away my tears of pain and brings joy to my heart restoring my faith by planting one small seed.

He wines and dines me spiritually, nourishing my body and mind using the finest ingredients to feed my soul.

He whispers softly how much he loves me; by my side always he will be, his love and comfort completes me and makes me whole.

He appreciates me, He respects me, He listens attentively when I speak, careful not to judge me or belittle me, or break me down or make me weak.

He showers me with precious gifts he fulfills my every desire, I got a man that holds my heart and sets my spirit a fire...

A Father figure...A Big brother...A Best friend he will always be.

Father God, my heart and my soul I deeply pledge to thee.

God's word says *"Put on the whole armor of God that you may be able to stand against the wiles of the devil." Ephesians 6:10-17* He explicitly lays out the wardrobe for spiritual warfare from head to toe; including the sword of the Spirit, which is the word of God and prayer, not only for self but all saints in the name of Jesus. Fight the good fight of faith. Stand firm and strong and be encouraged. Victory in Jesus is a reward and love that no man or woman on earth can ever provide. I dress to impress God and God only.

As a Warrior, I testify my Furious Faith., my deliverance from an abusive relationship and my desire to run this race. Seek ye first the kingdom of God and all these things shall be added unto you. For faith in God's word and his love are the weapons we need to seize and conquer.

Be Encouraged...

I Too Have a Dream
By: Charlotte E. Harris

The other day I heard a caller on the radio say "we need another Dr. Martin Luther King, Jr. – someone with a voice and some direction for Black people." As he continued to talk he said, "There's currently not that one person who is adequately representing nor addressing the needs of the African American community."

Well to the young man who made that statement and others who hold that same position – waiting for the next Dr. Martin Luther King, Jr., it's not going to happen. As God made only one of you, so did he make only one Dr. Martin Luther King, Jr. He was here for a season and a purpose to which he readily accepted and walked in. Additionally, could the person you are looking for to be the next Dr. Martin Luther King Jr. actually be you? Hum?

We were each created uniquely and specifically for a purpose. Scripture tells us that *"we are God's workmanship, created in Christ Jesus to do good works, which God prepared in advance for us to do."* (Ephesians 2:10) Sadly enough, many people live their whole lives never discovering or knowing what that purpose is. I believe that the not knowing is what makes us look for other people to step up and fix a broken system, problem, career, or country. We tend to think other people are more qualified, suited, or ready to fill a certain job than we are, thereby taking the pressure or ownership off of us. While we are busy rallying around the latest issues or blaming our elected leaders (on the local, national, or international levels) for not doing something right – we lose focus on our own purpose. We eventually find ourselves off and on many bandwagons- never finding our own destiny, our purpose.

Sometimes finding your purpose is easier than you think. As stated earlier, we were created to do good works which God prepared *in advance* for us to do. Dr. Martin Luther King Jr. was not born a "doctor" he had to work for it. At age five he joined his church; at age 14 he entered and won an oratorical contest on the subject, *The Negro and the Constitution;* in his late teens he worked two summers in Connecticut in a plant that hired both "Negroes and whites". He then said, "here I saw economic injustice firsthand, and realized that the poor white was exploited just as much as the Negro. Through these early experiences I grew up deeply conscious of the varieties of injustice in our society." Is it surprising that he would become a Civil Rights leader and give his life for the cause?

So, what good works were you created to accomplish? Think back to when you were a child - what did you want to be when you grew up? Was it a doctor, lawyer, teacher, engineer, cop – what? Why did you want to do this? Did you like helping people, making complex drawings, or keeping the bad guys off the street? More often than not that very thing we wanted to do before the world became so intimidating is the very thing we were created to do. Somehow it got lost along the way. We took our eyes off of the prize; life threw us some tough punches, knocked us down, but not out.

My sisters and brothers it is time to recapture that dream, your purpose. Scripture tells us that we can move forward by *forgetting what is behind and pressing on toward the mark for the prize of the high calling of God in Christ Jesus.* (Philippians 3:14)

As Dr. Martin Luther King had a dream, I too have a dream. I dream that all of God's children will walk in the splendor of His holiness. That we will do right because it's the right thing to do and not the popular thing to do.

I dream that when we see another brother or sister in need we will reach out to that brother or sister and not wait for someone else to come to the rescue (Thinking that someone else is going to do it never works because tomorrow never comes).

I dream that Christians everywhere will live a life that reflects Christ love:

We will be patient, we will be kind

We will not envy, we will not boast

We will not be proud, we will not be rude

We will not seek our own; we will not be easily angered

We will not keep records of wrongs; we will not delight in evil

We will rejoice with the truth; we will bear one another's burdens.

We will work on removing the plank from our own eye before attempting to remove the speck from our brother's eyes.

We will not let the sun go down on our anger but will make every effort to be reconciled to our brother.

We will consider others better than ourselves and put their needs above our own. You see, my dream is not only rooted in the American dream but in an eternal dream. My desire is that none should perish but have everlasting life with the Father.

In order for that to happen we Christians need to become a more compassionate people. A caring people, a forgiving people, a loving people. A people that will stand up for right, a people that will walk in the light. A people unashamed, a people that will call on Jesus Name. I too have a dream and so do you.

Charlotte Harris is an exciting woman of God. She taught the Word of God for over 15 years, through Sunday Schools, Bible Studies, seminars, etc. A native of Wilmington, Delaware, Charlotte enlisted in the United States Air Force and retired after 20+ years of honorable service. She earned a Masters Degree in Human Relations, and a Bachelors Degree in Business Management. She is the author of *Charlotte Speaks: Words of Wisdom to Live By* (Lulu.com, 2007) *and Mountains and Valleys* (Dorrance Publishing, 2004).

Contact Charlotte at: www.movingforwardnow.org email:
hrrs323@aol.com

Sources:

Carson, Clayborne, The Autobiography of Martin Luther King, Jr, Warner Books, Inc., January 2001

Faith Answered Those Calls
By: M.J.Holloway

As I pulled up to my uncle's house and put my car in park, the man who molested me during my childhood pulled up behind me. I got out of my car, locked my doors and heard the deep voice that I knew very well. "Hey girl how are you doing?" he asked me.

"Just fine," I answered, then asked, "Is that your baby?" As I walked toward his car, he began approaching me with his little one. Without a thought he hugged me and kissed my cheek and I never even cringed. As a matter of fact the thought never crossed my mind that it was him, the one who had violated my peace. In that moment I realized I was free, could this freedom have come from those phone calls a few years prior...

Out of the blue he began calling from the penitentiary. I wondered why he was calling me of all people, but in my heart I knew I should act in love even though I felt nothing that resembled my actions. Even though I didn't know what to say, I had to accept his calls and make small talk with the person who stole so much from my life. Our conversations were always brief and to the point; our families were close and that was our common ground.

Every time he called, my body cringed. In my mind I wanted to curse him and ask the famous question, "Why did you do that to me? You caused me so much pain and heartache and unnecessary anxiety." I desperately wanted to ask him, "Why are you calling my house?" I felt powerless; I didn't know what to do. I didn't know why he was tormenting me. How could I make him stop! During our conversations I wanted to ask, "Why did you steal my inner peace, a part of me that could never be replaced?" But my resistance to acknowledge the nightmare that had taken place allowed me to be passive in my conversation with him. He could have called many other people who would have listened to him with pure motives, but my heart just wasn't there yet. I wanted to be the angry victim. I wished I could be vindictive enough to plot revenge, because my mind was still stuck on what he had done to me.

Thinking back I know I should have told long time ago; I should have told the very first night it happened. I knew if I told many people would have been hurt. So I found myself worrying about everyone else's needs and not my own. I felt embarrassed about what I would have to go through, if I told what happened and I knew it would hurt my family. I was scared that our families' relationships would be destroyed. I didn't know if he would tell the truth; to this day, he still acts as though nothing ever happened. I didn't even know if his mom would believe me about her son. I didn't want to be responsible for the division my secret might bring to our families.

Right when my dreams were coming true the calls started. At the time, I was a twenty-five year old single mother. I enjoyed working with the mentally challenged and finally I was not struggling financially. For the first time since becoming a mother I was able to take care of my son. I was feeling pretty confident about myself and my relationship with God. I could see things changing in my life and meeting Ken allowed me to see my dream of a complete family coming true.

Once the calls started however, a feeling of sadness began to come alive deep within my heart. I tried to totally focus on the wedding and the great changes that were happening to me, but my mind was in turmoil. I knew somehow I had to bring closure to this secret of my past in order to start my new life with Ken. Those phone calls seemed to stir up emotions because they reminded me that the secret was becoming a part of my life in reality.

Each time he called we were only able to talk four to five minutes at a time before the phone would cut off. After every hang-up my mind began to reminisce about that part of my childhood. I thought about the constant fear I felt each time we had to spend the night at their house. Sometimes when my mom needed a sitter she would leave us with them, and during the ride to their house I would develop my game plan to stay up all night long. If I fell asleep, I would be awakened by him fondling me or my panties being down to my ankles. It is my guess that he didn't know how to stop himself from fondling and molesting me.

Though I tried to hold on to the pain, after the calls started, I felt like I couldn't live unless I talked to someone about this. I knew there was a risk if I told someone other than my roommate, but I had to tell. I knew this would require faith; faith I wasn't sure I had within me, but I had to tell my fiancé' and my mother.

I told Ken first because he knew that something was bothering me. I didn't want to start our marriage with secrets. But I knew this conversation would put my trust in God to the test, so with faith in my heart and hope in my eyes I looked the man of my dreams right in his eyes while we stood in my kitchen. I shared my heart with him, not knowing the end result or his response. To my surprise the man I love did not respond in anger as I expected. We stood, face to face as he looked into my eyes and spoke the words, that I thank God for even 'til this day. "I love you and this doesn't change anything for us." I expected him to flee and escape our love, but he never did and he never has.

Since I felt liberated by telling Ken, I knew I had to tell my mother. The next morning I stood in the same kitchen at my window from the night before, picked up my cordless phone and began to press the digits that would connect me to my mother for one of the most serious conversations that I would ever have with her. My heart was pounding and racing at the same time, but the greatest part was I knew God was with me.

I did not know what her response would be, but I definitely felt motivation from the Holy Spirit. As the phone dialed and my mother answered, our conversation started out as usual, but I quickly went straight to the point.

I could not think of any great way to break the news so I just said it, "Mom I was molested by someone close to us and to what extent I truly do not know. Most of the time I woke up with my panties just down, very seldom did I actually see him, but I knew it was him."

At that moment, I felt thousands of miles away from my mother because her silence created distance. I knew she was still on the other end and actually just ten miles down the road. I wanted her to express some emotion, but I should have known what to expect from the woman who taught her children to keep the peace. I knew she would not rock any boats because she couldn't, it was not in her. But it still hurt because just for one moment, even if she never really acted on her anger, I wanted her to act it out for me.

I don't quite remember her exact words but I decided in my heart I was not going to get stuck their. I chose to focus on the fact that I had finally told the secret. It was not mine anymore. It took years for my mother and I to really talk about what had happened and I found out that she just did not know how to respond. She felt like somehow she had failed me.

What is funny to me now is that I do not quite remember when or how the phone calls ended, it seems like once I walked down this process of hope and faith they just stopped. I know the phone calls gave me the opportunity to face my past and to have faith in my future. The residue from my past as painful as the memories were, show me the importance of forgiveness. Through those calls God enable me to overcome a piece of the past in my life that had me bound and wounded for years.

God doesn't create situations that hurt us or that may bring us pain; he just takes the opportunity to walk us from defeat to victory. I may never forget (I believe God that I will), but one thing is for sure, I am no longer controlled by the untold secret.

I have often wondered what price he paid for what he did to me. I know what I lost and now what I have gained. It took a lot of faith for me to accept his collect phone calls and to risk my relationship with my fiancé' (who would want to marry somebody with my kind of freaky past?) It was an unusual thing to share intimate issues by opening up my past and sharing my heart with Ken. The past that had been off limits to any one, and I thank God I did it. A long time ago I chose by faith to forgive this person for what happened, and because of Gods love I know he will deliver this young man by giving him the same liberty and freedom that he has so graciously sown into me.

M.J. Holloway is an author, poet, and teacher. She is also the co-pastor of Kingdom Life Christian Center of Dayton, OH. Co-Pastor Holloway is a woman that loves her family, and her God.
Contact Co-Pastor Holloway at: (937) 401-4490/ e-mail:
peachesholloway1@aol.com

God Has Promised
By: Penda L. James

Evidently motherhood changes a girl into a woman. It sounds like a cliché, but my pregnancy forced me to elevate my eyes to the Father; it compelled me to stand on a faith I didn't recognize was in me. Becoming a mother required me to stand on my talk, and walk as a true believer. I had no choice if not for me, but for my child to believe.

Our struggles the first year as a married couple were mostly financial. The carry over of that burden shook my theology — I loved God, but I always worried about money. Robert was a full-time youth pastor and I was a part-time admissions counselor. Our checks barely brought in enough money to cover our bills and keep the refrigerator stocked. With no money to build a savings, we paid our tithes faithfully often leaving only pennies to spare after all obligations were met.

For a long time we yearned for a change. The atmosphere in our home was often tense and quiet, we created a sanctuary, but brought our frustrations home to each other. We felt like hamsters in a cage, if we weren't running on the stationary wheel we were scratching at the bars trying to escape. I wanted to find a job that would allow me to work normal hours, not weekends and evenings away from my new husband. Robert wanted to fully operate in his gifts, to walk with a ministry that supported his vision for young people. In faith we both applied for jobs across the country. The deal was that we'd move to accommodate whoever got a job first.

When he got the offer, he called me right away, "put in your resignation for Friday." He was so excited that he wasn't breathing.

"What?" I was half listening, half typing on the computer.

"I got the job at Mt. Ararat."

178

I dropped the phone then picked it back up, "Wait. What did you say?"

"We're moving to Pittsburgh and I have to be there on Sunday." It was Tuesday and Sunday was Mother's Day. I remember sitting at my desk with my head spinning. I was so excited for our fresh start in a new state that it never crossed my mind that the move was uprooting me from my family and friends. Not at all did I think about the impact of leaving my comfort zone.

My resignation letter was already written, lacking only the date. I pulled it up on my screen, printed it and walked into my supervisor's office. "Two weeks from Friday will be my last day." I sat on the chair across from her desk and cried because I had so many emotions that I could not contain myself. I was sad, but the feeling of liberation outweighed the sadness, we were finally going to be free from the cage!

I stayed in Dayton for two months to tie up loose ends and care for my nephew while my sister was away at military training. The church put Robert up in a hotel, assisted us in finding housing and tried to help me find a job. For two months he commuted back and forth, paid the mortgage in Ohio, and rent in Pennsylvania. Because I was not working he alternated each month between paying the two car payments, our student loans and other bills.

When we were reunited in Pittsburgh, I was optimistic. It was the summer and I loved our new house. I thought our landlord was so sweet, but behind closed doors she would do things like re-hang our clothes on the clothes line or enter our house without our permission! Once she even walked in on me when I was in the bed sick and told me to eat some chicken noodle soup.

I was applying for jobs but no one was calling me back. I was discouraged, but I was also transforming. I would be happy one minute and sad the next. I'd sit down on the couch and wake up two hours later. I ate six oranges a day and sometimes I ate six times a day. I cried a lot and my stomach hurt. A part of me thought I was pregnant, but I was afraid to go to the doctor for fear of adding more bills. My prayer was, "God you know what I need."

After six months I had found a part time job, but it wasn't enough. We had bills piled up to the ceiling and we had to ignore the phone for creditors harassing us for money we didn't have. The stress of our landlord and the unpaid bills was too much, I wanted to move back to Dayton, so my husband found a nicer landlord and we moved that December.

Funny things started happening after the move. It started with two very dramatic falls. One was when my ankle gave out and I stumbled across the street into the neighbor's yard. I thought it was an old volleyball injury. The two women who saw me fall didn't help me; I guess they thought I was intoxicated so they kept walking. The other time I slipped on the balcony steps at church and landed directly on the center of my stomach, during the pastor's sermon! It hurt, but out of embarrassment I got up and sat in my seat.

For Christmas I went home to see my family and my sister kept her eyes on my stomach. She advised me to take a pregnancy test because "it looked funny" to her. Because I had endometriosis, I thought I couldn't get pregnant, my symptoms were passed off as emotional distress from moving, but when I took the test and it was positive I couldn't believe it. Everything began to make sense, the constipation, the flutters, the emotional roller coasters and the oranges.

A week later I was on my way home from work when I was rear-ended by a member of the church on her way to a meeting. The police didn't come, but out of precaution my husband took me to the hospital. The ultrasound showed that I was twenty-eight weeks! I had been pregnant for six months and didn't know it, in less than three months the baby was coming. Her actual due date was April 28th.

People made comments that my baby would be deformed and sickly because I hadn't had prenatal care, but I stood on the Word of God that all things work together for good to them that love the Lord and are the called according to His purpose. Not only that, we had nothing prepared for a baby, but I trusted that God wouldn't put us in that situation and not provide.

The three months before she was born were chaotic. I was in and out of the hospital because my blood pressure was high. For weeks I was tested for preeclapsia, a condition that occurs when blood pressure rises in pregnant women. The doctor told me that my baby could die, but she "wasn't trying to scare me." I was advised to exercise because my obesity was the cause of my hypertension when truthfully, hypertension is hereditary. They told me to stop working and I complied with a compromise, two hours a day.

I trusted God; I would not let them create images in my mind about my child who God Himself planted when I wasn't even trying to get pregnant. Every week they tested my protein and when the results came back I'd smile and say, "I told you I wasn't preeclamptic." For a month I had appointments twice a week and on March 19th I went in for a routine appointment and was admitted. My blood pressure was 167 over 112. The doctors told me that they would have to induce my labor to prevent me from having a seizure. I was told all of the bad things that could happen to the baby, but I didn't receive them.

When she was born, she was jaundiced, and couldn't eat for two days due to the magnesium they used to lower my blood pressure. We were told that she could be in the hospital for a month, and that there was a possibility that her hair could be shaved if her veins collapsed. Whenever I could, I went to her bedside and played with her toes. I spoke the Word of God to her and played classical music in her room. I can't say that I didn't ask a lot of questions of God, but I became a warrior for my daughter because she had been protected from hurt harm and danger in my womb. Not only did I not know I was pregnant until I was six months, I fell twice and had a car accident, a little boy ran into my stomach head first. I owed my baby my faith; I had to believe that she would live.

Amaris was only in the hospital for nine days. I knew the strength of my baby that's why her name means *"God has promised a strong tower."* Everyone else was amazed that she matured so quickly. She's a little underweight but she's healthy and whole like I knew she would be. I watch her and she's a strong little girl. She kicks her legs like a karate champion and sets her focus on getting what she needs. The favor that is on her life is already amazing. We didn't have to buy anything for her the first few months, everything from my maternity clothes to her entire wardrobe; car seats, strollers and a bed were all gifted to us. She has clothes to last at least a year for every season and size!

We still have bills, but I learned to stand on faith because of my daughter. Nothing that anyone said aside from words of life meant anything to me when it came to her. It wasn't easy, but in the end I called God on His promises in a way I had never exercised before. I asked my Father to protect us and He did while using motherhood to change my priorities. Fretting about small things only makes matters worse, but the substance of things hoped for and the evidence of things not seen is where the promise lies. He said He would provide our need according to His riches and glory; we have been good stewards and we continue to wait for the promise that our latter will be greater. Motherhood taught me to believe the truth of that statement.

Penda L. James, a graduate of Wilberforce University (B.A.) and Bowling Green State University (M.Ed) has been passionate about writing and reading since she was a child. Introduced to Maya Angelou by her grandmother, Penda learned the power of words to give readers hope and strength. She resides in Pittsburgh with her husband and daughter where she enjoys coaching writers and working with youth. Other Projects include: Free to Fly: Reflections on Womanhood (Chapbook, 2000). Free to Fly: Wisdom for the Seasons in a Woman's Life (Coming Fall 2008).

Contact Penda at: email: pljames_scribe@yahoo.com

About the editor

Vanessa Miller of Dayton, Ohio is a best-selling author, playwright, and motivational speaker. Her stage productions include: **Get You Some Business, Don't Turn Your Back on God,** and **Can't You Hear Them Crying.** Vanessa is currently in the process of turning the novels in the Rain Series into stage productions.

Vanessa has been writing since she was a young child. When she wasn't reading, writing poetry, short stories, stage plays and novels consumed her free time. However, it wasn't until she committed her life to the Lord in 1994 that she realized all gifts and anointing come from God. She then set out to write redemption stories that glorified God.

To date, Vanessa has written the Rain Series and the Storm Series. The books in the Rain Series are: **Former Rain, Abundant Rain,** and **Latter Rain**. The books in the Storm Series are: **Rain Storm** and **Through The Storm.** These books have received rave reviews, winning Best Christian Fiction Awards and topping numerous Bestseller's lists. Vanessa believes that each book in The Rain and Storm Series will touch readers across the country in a special way. It is, after all her God-given destiny to write and produce plays and novels that bring deliverance to God's people.

Vanessa self-published her first three books, then in 2006 she signed a five-book deal with Urban Christian/Kensington. Her books can now be found in Wal-Mart, most all major bookstores, including African American bookstores and online bookstores such as Amazon.com.

Vanessa is a dedicated Christian and devoted mother. She graduated from Capital University with a degree in Organizational Communication. In 2007 Vanessa was ordained by her church as an exhorter. Which of course, Vanessa believes was the right position for her because God has called her to exhort readers and to help them rediscover their place with the Lord.

A perfect day for Vanessa is one that affords her the time to curl up with a good book. She is currently working on the **Live Right or Die Trying Series**. The books in this series, although they can be categorized as suspense thrillers, will still have elements of God's redemptive power throughout the stories. She is also preparing the stage production for the **Former Rain** novel.

CALLING ALL ENTREPRENEURS, AUTHORS & FAITH WALKERS

The second installment in the Faith anthology series will be *Stepping Out On Faith*. This anthology is for entrepreneurs that have stepped out on faith and gone into ministry, started a company, or wrote the book/released the CD that was in their hearts. If you are an entrepreneur and would like to encourage others to follow their dreams then you will want to be a part of the **Stepping Out On Faith** anthology.

The third and final installment in the Faith anthology series will be *Have A Little Faith*. This anthology is designed for those individuals that have gone through test and trials and come out on the right side of FAITH. Have you or anyone in your family ever been healed of an illness, delivered from an addiction, or set free from sin all in the name of Jesus. If you have, then you most certainly must *Have A Little Faith*, and we need you for this anthology.

If you would like more information on the *Stepping Out On Faith* or the *Have A Little Faith* anthology please contact me at: vmiller-01@earthlink.net. The subject line of your email should say: *Stepping Out On Faith* or *Have A Little Faith*.

Check out these other Books by Vanessa Miller

The Rain Series

Purchase the Rain Series at:

Bookstores Everywhere
Walmart
www.amazon.com
Black Expression Book Club
www.MochaReaders.com

Check out these Books by Vanessa Miller

The Storm Series

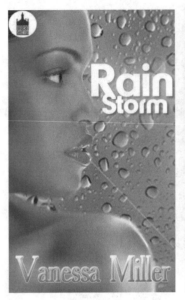 

Purchase the Storm Series at:

Bookstores Everywhere
Walmart
www.amazon.com
Black Expression Book Club
www.MochaReaders.com

Check out these books by Kim Jackson

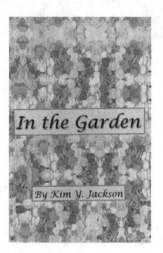

Purchase these books at:

www.kimyjackson.com